CW00433208

Big Blue Planet

and other songs for worship in God's world

For young children to share with everyone

edited by Judy Jarvis

illustrated by Jan Nesbitt

Stainer & Bell

First published in 1995 by Stainer & Bell Limited and The Methodist Church Division of Education and Youth
Reprinted in 2000 by Stainer & Bell Limited

All rights reserved. This book and each copyright item within it is copyright under the Berne Convention.
It is fully protected by The British Copyright, Designs and Patents Act 1988.

Compilation, prefatory material, typography, music setting and illustrations
© 1995 Stainer & Bell Ltd and The Trustees for Methodist Church Purposes.

Copyright in words and music of each song is indicated alongside each item. The addresses of the copyright holders are:

Linda Caroe, 20 Prideaux Road, Eastbourne, Sussex BN21 2NB
Church of Scotland/St Andrew's Press, St Colm's Centre, 20/23 Inverleith Terrace, Edinburgh EH3 5NX
Cyhoeddiadau Curiad, The Old Library, County Road, Pen-y-Groes, Caernarfon, Gwynedd LL454 6EY
Daybreak Music Ltd, 4 Regency Mews, Silverdale Road, Eastbourne, Sussex BN20 7AB
GIA Publications Inc, 7404 S. Mason Avenue, Chicago, Illinois 60638, USA
Hope Publishing Company, 380 South Main Place, Carol Stream, Ilinois 60188, USA
Iona Community/Wild Goose Publications, Community House, Pearce Institute, Govan, Glasgow G51 3UT
Jubilate Hymns Limited, 4 Thorne Park Road, Chelston, Torquay TQ2 6RX
Kevin Mayhew Ltd, Rattlesden, Bury St Edmunds, Suffolk IP30 0SZ
The National Society (re. Red Lentil Music), Church House, Great Smith Street, London SW1P 3NZ
Salvationist Publishing and Supplies Ltd, 117-121 Judd Street, London WC1H 9NN
Scripture Press Publications Inc, 4050 Lee Vance View, Colorado Springs, CO80198, USA
Stainer & Bell Ltd, PO Box 110, Victoria House, 23 Gruneisen Road, London N3 1DZ
Sunday School Society for Ireland, Holy Trinity Church, Church Avenue, Rathmines, Dublin 6, Irish Republic
The Trustees for Methodist Church Purposes (Copyright enquiries should be addressed to Stainer & Bell Ltd)

No copyright words or music may be reproduced, stored in a retrieval system, or transmitted in any form, or by any means, electronic, mechanical,
recording or otherwise without the prior permission of the administrator of the individual item concerned.

No typography, music setting, or other graphic material may be stored in a retrieval system, copied using an photocopying process or by other means
of reflecting the visual image of the printed page by use, for example, of an overhead projector or epidiascope without the prior permission of Stainer & Bell Ltd.

Words where Stainer & Bell Ltd are copyright holders or co-copyright holders may as at the date of publication be copied by those holding a current
Christian Copyright Licensing Ltd words licence provided the items copied are included on their returns. Other words may only be copied if the copyright administrator is
a member of the CCLI scheme and in accordance with the terms and conditions laid down by that administrator.

This book is included in the Christian Copyright Licensing Ltd "Music Reproduction Licence" at the date of this printing and holders of this licence may copy items
subject to the terms of that licence provided that the copyright administrator is also a member of this scheme.

British Library Cataloguing-in-Publication Data
A catalogue record for this book is available from the British Library.

ISBN 0 85249 827 6
ISMN M 2202 0125 7

A Welsh edition of this book (Glas Glas Blaned) is published by Cyhoeddiadau'r Gair (Council for Sunday Schools & Christian Education in Wales): ISBN 1 85994 038 2

Printed in Great Britain by Caligraving Ltd, Thetford

CONTENTS

INTRODUCTION

There were three little owls in a wood
Who sang hymns whenever they could;
What the words were about
One could never make out
But one felt it was doing them good.

Anonymous

Unlike those songs enjoyed by the three little owls, the songs in BIG BLUE PLANET should not only do people good but be understood by everyone: young children, their older brothers and sisters and friends, and adults of all ages. It is hoped that they will prove beneficial to those who use them by meeting their needs and complementing their experiences. But this will only happen if the songs enable them to make connections with the important issues of today's world.

This thought was the guiding principle for the group gathered from many churches and organisations which make up the CGMC – the Consultative Group on Ministry among Children (see p. viii) – to collect material for BIG BLUE PLANET. From the start, their diversity of interests and cultural backgrounds, including members from England, Ireland, Scotland and Wales, was a special inspiration in the book's lively development. However, it was the growing sense during the work that the project might concern the whole of God's created world, its problems, challenges and rewards in our own age, that gave the book its special sense of direction – and its title.

Perennial themes such as the seasons and church festivals are linked with contemporary ideas and modes of feeling. Subject matter ranges from the microchip to the fragile 'big blue planet' itself, and from the age of dinosaurs to the era of fast food, computers and motorway madness. The music reflects this plurality of ideas in its own variety of styles from past and present, culled from folk and popular traditions. Many of these songs are newly composed and presented here for the first time alongside firm favourites. A stimulus to explore and experiment, they can nevertheless be learnt in a few minutes; and some, it is hoped, will soon be learnt by heart.

A Welsh edition of BIG BLUE PLANET, published as GLAS GLAS BLANED, gives this song collection an additional relevance and usefulness to a host of potential users. Above all, the aim has been to encourage children and adults to worship in whichever way comes naturally to them. In pursuing this objective the members of my advisory group – June Baker, George Bexon, Aled Davies, Andrew E Pratt, Ionwen Roberts, Marion Saunders, Christine Tulloch and Delyth Wyn, with the additional help of Heather Wilkinson – have been a constant source of strength and encouragement. While the final choice of material was my own, it is their rich fund of expertise so freely offered that is the true strength of this book.

Judy Jarvis
London, May 1995

SOME GUIDELINES FOR TEACHING THE SONGS

1 Use your voice to teach the songs, especially if you are a woman. Young children can pick up a melody more quickly from the human voice, and a woman's pitch is closer to their own.

2 Learn a song well before you try to teach it. Practise it on your children, the cat, or anyone else who is prepared to listen.

3 It's better if you are not too good! You won't make other people feel inadequate. However, it does help to be able to sing in tune - and be prepared to explain to children what this means as well.

4 Allow for the fact that children will learn more quickly than adults, who have often forgotten how to learn things by heart.

5 Remember that many young children who read well still need to concentrate hard on their reading, and therefore may find it hard to sing enthusiastically at the same time. There are also some adults who have difficulty in reading.

6 If children and adults do not bury their faces in a book it is much easier for them to breathe properly and sing well. It is also more fun.

7 Don't be afraid to use your hands to show where the tune goes up and down - and don't be surprised if children copy you!

8 Don't worry if you have nobody to accompany you. Almost all the songs can be sung unaccompanied, and singing without accompaniment makes for variety.

9 Teach a new song before worship begins, so that the flow of the worship is not interrupted.

10 Encourage children (and adults) to add verses and actions of their own if they wish.

11 Don't force adults to join in songs which are better sung by children in their own groups.

12 Make it clear when all ages are together that the song is for everybody. No-one is too young or too old to join in. Nobody's voice is too frail or out of tune.

13 Encourage both children and adults to use percussion. Let them do it freely and without inhibition - but not all at once.

14 Enjoy your task. Share your enjoyment and enthusiasm with others of all ages.

The following churches and bodies make up the membership of the Consultative Group on Ministry among children - a network of CCBI (the Council of Churches in Britain and Ireland).

Baptist Union of Great Britain
Catholic Education Commission - Scotland
Christian Aid
Christian Education Movement
Church of England
Church of Ireland
Church of Scotland
Church in Wales
Churches' Commission on Mission
Congregational Federation
Council of African & Afro-Caribbean Churches UK
Council for Sunday Schools & Christian Education in Wales
Independent Methodist Churches - Young People's Department

Irish Methodist Department of Youth and Children's Work
The Methodist Church
National Christian Education Council
New Testament Assembly
New Testament Church of God
Presbyterian Church in Wales
Quaker Home Service
Roman Catholic Church
Salvation Army
Scottish Sunday School Union
Sunday School Scoiety for Ireland
United Reformed Church
Welsh National Centre for Religious Education

EVERY DAY

1 ALWAYS REMEMBER, NEVER FORGET

Lynda Masson (1951–)

With a swing

Always remember, never forget
Never forget to say THANK YOU!
Always remember, never forget
Always say Thank you Lord.

1   Thank you for food to eat
    For clothes to wear, shoes on our feet.
    Chorus

2   Thank you for health today
    For strength to work and run and play.
    Chorus

3   Thank you for a place to stay
    For warmth and comfort day by day.
    Chorus

Lynda Masson (1951–)

Words and Music © 1995 Stainer & Bell Ltd and The Trustees for Methodist Church Purposes

Clap to the music to learn it before adding the words. Clap or nod at the rest before THANK YOU. It's fun to sing 'thank you' louder than the other words.

2 JUBILATE DEO

Sylvia Crowther (1946–)

1   Jubilate Deo,
    Jubilate Deo,
    Jubilate Deo,
    Amen.

2   Thank you for the sunshine,
    Thank you for the rain,
    Thank you God for everything,
    Amen.

Verse 1: Traditional
Verse 2: Sylvia Crowther (1946–)

Music and Words of Verse 2 © 1995 Stainer & Bell Ltd and The Trustees for Methodist Church Purposes

The first verse is a song of praise which all ages can share, including very young children, who love strange-sounding words.

3 LET US PRAISE THE LORD OUR GOD

Sylvia Crowther (1946–)

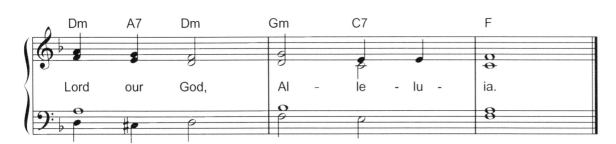

Let us praise the Lord our God,
Let us praise the Lord our God,
Let us praise the Lord our God,
Alleluia.

Albert Jewell (1936–)

Words and Music © 1995 Stainer & Bell Ltd and The Trustees for Methodist Church Purposes

A song for everyone. Try a single clap and raising both arms in the air on 'Alleluia'.

4 *LORD HEAR OUR PRAYER*

Sylvia Crowther (1946–)

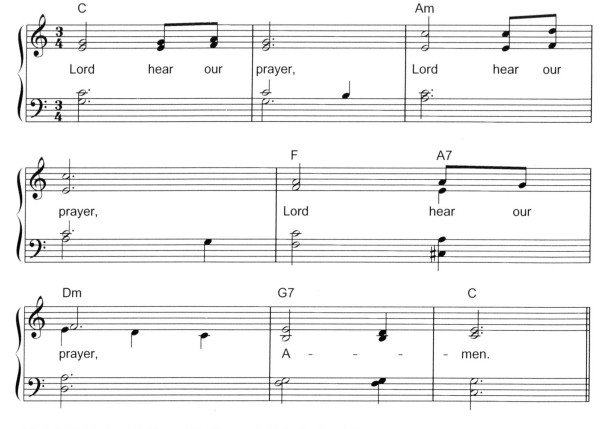

Lord hear our prayer,
Lord hear our prayer,
Lord hear our prayer,
Amen.

Traditional

Music © 1995 Stainer & Bell Ltd and The Trustees for Methodist Church Purposes

Use for all ages during, or at the end of, prayers for others.

5 LET TODAY BE THE DAY

Judith Franklin (1947–)
arranged June Baker (1936–)

1 Let today be the day as I go along my way,
Let today be the day to be happy.
And let other people see
The love that is in me,
Let today be the day to be happy.

2 Let today be the day as I go along my way,
Let today be the day to be caring,
And let other people see
The love that is in me
Let today be the day to be caring.

Judith Franklin (1947–)

Words and Music © 1995 Stainer & Bell Ltd and The Trustees for Methodist Church Purposes

Ask the children to make 'happy faces' fastened to sticks to use in the first verse. Use the verses separately to link with different themes. More can be made up by the children, using 'ing' words such as praying, sharing.

6 ANNWYL IESU, DIOLCH I TI
LOVING JESUS, WE WILL THANK YOU

Ceri Gwyn (1964–)

1 Annwyl Iesu, diolch i ti,
Diwrnod arall hapus ges i;
Cofia am y plant sy'n dioddef:
Gad i ni deimlo'th gariad di.

2 Annwyl Iesu, buost gyda mi —
Diwrnod hir ac anodd ges i:
Cofia am bob un sy'n dioddef
Gad i ni deimlo'th gariad di.

Verse 1 by Ceri Gwyn (1964–)
Verse 2 by Delyth Wyn (1961–)

1 Loving Jesus, we will thank you
For another wonderful day;
Please remember those who suffer.
Let us all know your love each day.

2 Loving Jesus, you were near us
Through this dark and difficult day.
Please remember those who suffer.
Let us all know your love each day.

English Paraphrase: verse 1 by Delyth Wyn (1961–)
Verse 2 by Judy Jarvis (1940–)

Lyrics under music:
An - nwyl Ie - su, di - olch i____ ti,
Lov - ing Jes - us, we will thank____ you

Diwr - nod a - rall ha - pus ges i;
For an - oth - er won - der - ful day;

Co - fia am____ y plant sy'n dio - ddef:
Please re - mem - ber those who suf - fer.

Gad i ni deim - lo'th gar - iad di.
Let us all know your love each day.

Words and Music © 1995 Stainer & Bell Ltd and The Trustees for Methodist Church Purposes

A prayer for the end of the day. Choose whichever verse is most appropriate.

7 HE CAME DOWN

Music origin unknown
arranged John Bell (1949–)

Brightly

1   He came down that we may have love;
    He came down that we may have love;
    He came down that we may have love;
    Hallelujah for evermore.
    (repeat verse)

2   He came down that we may have peace;
    He came down that we may have peace;
    He came down that we may have peace;
    Hallelujah for evermore.
    (repeat verse)

3   He came down that we may have joy;
    He came down that we may have joy;
    He came down that we may have joy;
    Hallelujah for evermore.
    (repeat verse)

Traditional

© 1990 Wild Goose Resource Group, Iona Community, Glasgow, Scotland. Used by permission of GIA Publications Inc, Chicago, Illinois, exclusive agent for USA and Canada and of the Iona Community for the rest of the world.

Ask someone to sing each verse through and invite everyone to sing it straight back in reply. This works well with all ages. Young children enjoy this song as a circle dance — step to the right on the first line, to the left on the second line, to the right on the third line, to the centre on the fourth line, raising joined arms to meet together.

8 CARING, SHARING

Linda Caroe (1952–)
arranged Jeanne Harper

1 Caring, (caring), sharing, (sharing),
Loving, (loving), giving, (giving),
Living the Jesus way.

2 Seeing, (seeing), helping, (helping),
Loving, (loving), trusting, (trusting),
Living the Jesus way.

3 Praying, (praying), obeying, (obeying),
Loving, (loving), forgiving, (forgiving),
Living the Jesus way.

Linda Caroe (1952–)

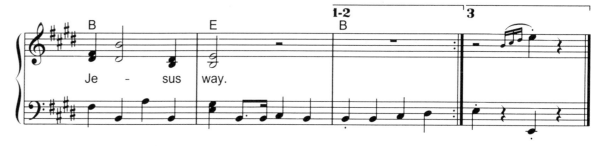

Words and Music © 1986 Linda Caroe, 20 Prideaux Road, Eastbourne, Sussex. Used by permission.

This song can be sung by the leader with children echoing or by two groups of children, the older ones taking the lead. It is also suitable for all ages. Ask the children to suggest simple actions.

9 BLESSING AND HONOUR

Brian Hoare (1935–)

Blessing and honour,
Glory and power
Are rightly yours,
All gracious God.

Music © 1994 Brian Hoare/Jubilate Hymns for world excluding USA and Canada. © Hope Publishing Company, Carol Stream, IL 60188 for USA and Canada. Words used by permission of the Faith and Order Committee of the Methodist Church.

This song is for everyone in the church community to share, particularly in the context of Holy Communion.

10 I NEARLY FORGOT TO SAY 'THANK YOU!'

John Larsson (1938–)

Moderato ♩ = 72

ad lib.

I near-ly for-got__ to say, 'Thank you!' For flow-ers and thrush-es and things, For dais-ies that dap-ple the mea-dow, And pat-terns on but-ter-fly wings, For stars that shine, for winds that blow,__ The sun that melts the ice and snow;__ I near-ly for-got__ to say, 'Thank you!' For rain-bows that fol-low the rain; But real-ly I want__ to say: 'Thank you!' A-gain and a-gain__ and a-gain. -gain.

Words and Music © Salvationist Publishing and Supplies Ltd. Used by permission.

I nearly forgot to say, 'Thank you!'
For flowers and thrushes and things,
For daisies that dapple the meadow,
And patterns on butterfly wings,
For stars that shine, for winds that blow,
The sun that melts the ice and snow;
I nearly forgot to say; 'Thank you!'
For rainbows that follow the rain;
But really I want to say: 'Thank you!'
Again and again and again.

John Gowans (1934–)

Younger children can join with each 'thank you' and 'again and again and again'. The song would fit very well with the story of the Samaritan leper (Luke 17) who returned to thank Jesus.

11 RIDING IN A CAR ON THE MOTORWAY

June Baker (1936–)

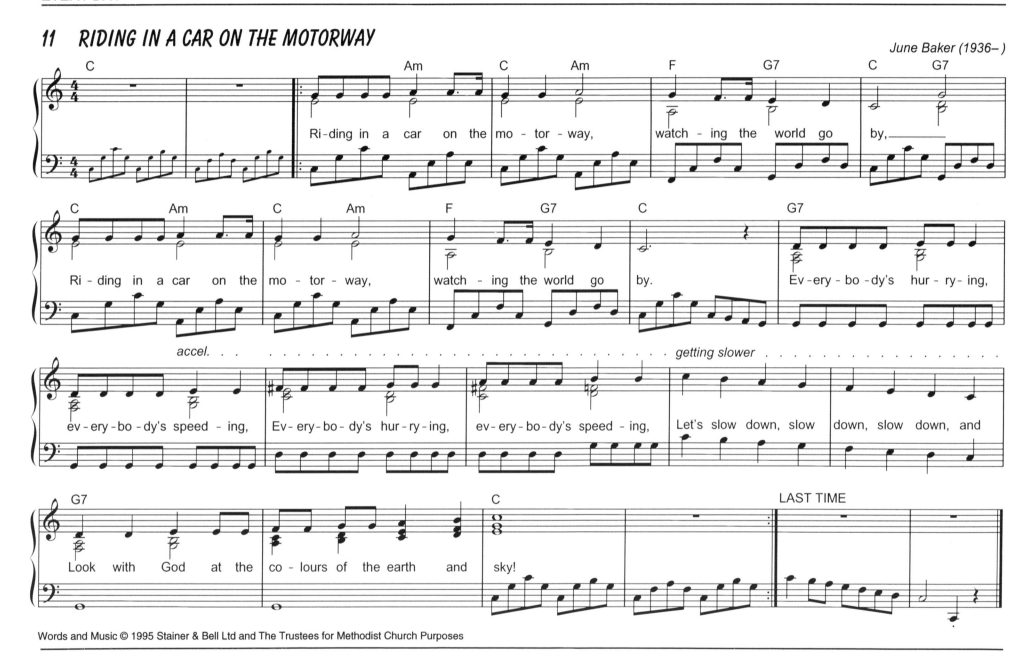

Ri-ding in a car on the mo-tor-way, watch-ing the world go by,____

Ri-ding in a car on the mo-tor-way, watch-ing the world go by. Ev-ery-bo-dy's hur-ry-ing,

accel. . . . ev-ery-bo-dy's speed-ing, Ev-ery-bo-dy's hur-ry-ing, ev-ery-bo-dy's speed-ing, *getting slower . . . .* Let's slow down, slow down, slow down, and

Look with God at the co-lours of the earth and sky!

LAST TIME

Words and Music © 1995 Stainer & Bell Ltd and The Trustees for Methodist Church Purposes

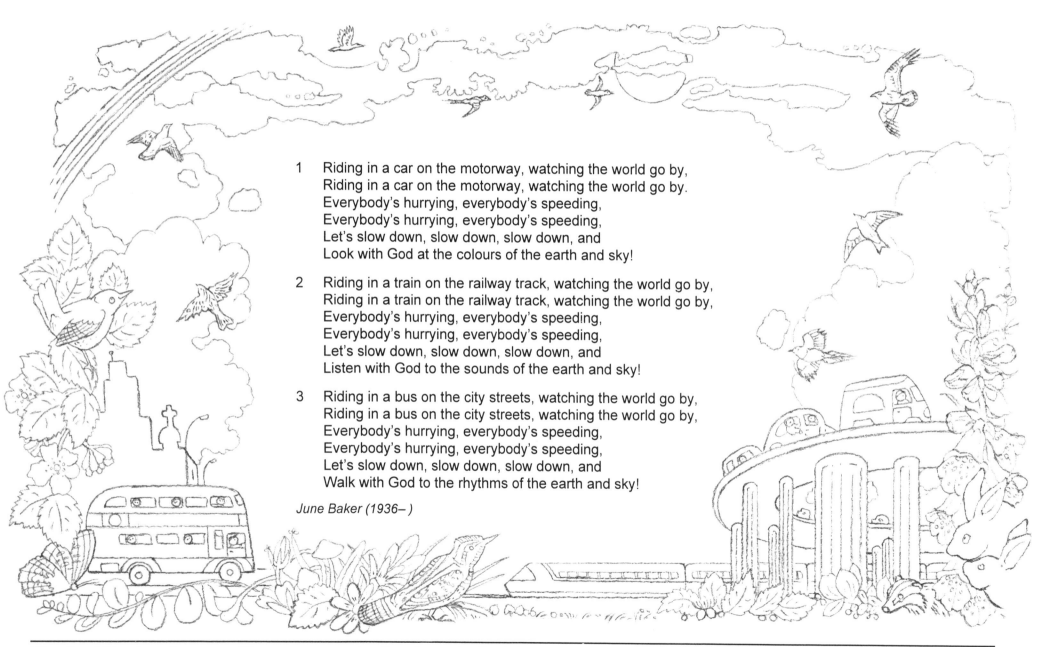

1   Riding in a car on the motorway, watching the world go by,
    Riding in a car on the motorway, watching the world go by.
    Everybody's hurrying, everybody's speeding,
    Everybody's hurrying, everybody's speeding,
    Let's slow down, slow down, slow down, and
    Look with God at the colours of the earth and sky!

2   Riding in a train on the railway track, watching the world go by,
    Riding in a train on the railway track, watching the world go by,
    Everybody's hurrying, everybody's speeding,
    Everybody's hurrying, everybody's speeding,
    Let's slow down, slow down, slow down, and
    Listen with God to the sounds of the earth and sky!

3   Riding in a bus on the city streets, watching the world go by,
    Riding in a bus on the city streets, watching the world go by,
    Everybody's hurrying, everybody's speeding,
    Everybody's hurrying, everybody's speeding,
    Let's slow down, slow down, slow down, and
    Walk with God to the rhythms of the earth and sky!

June Baker (1936–)

When the children know the song well they can run around as they sing, pretending to be cars, trains and buses, slowing right down and looking around them during the last two lines of each verse. Alternatively, two groups can take it in turns to sing and act.

12 PRAISE THE LORD OF ALL CREATION

Melody by St. Michael's Junior Choir, Limerick
arranged Harry Grindle (1935–)

1   Praise the Lord of all creation,
Praise the Lord for all his works.
Alleluia, Alleluia, Alleluia,
Praise the Lord.

2   Praise the Lord for all our blessings,
Praise the Lord who loves us all.
Alleluia, Alleluia, Alleluia,
Glóir duit a Thiarna. *(Irish)*

3   Praise the Lord for fathers and mothers,
Praise the Lord for all our friends.
Alleluia, Alleluia, Alleluia,
Molaibh an Tighearna. *(Scottish-Gaelic)*

4   Praise the Lord for he is loving,
Praise the Lord for being our Lord.
Alleluia, Alleluia, Alleluia,
Molwch Dduw. *(Welsh)*

St Michael's Junior Choir, Limerick

Words and Music reprinted by permission of the Sunday School Society for Ireland

Use this song to celebrate England, Scotland, Ireland and Wales—different countries, yet living and worshipping together.

STORY DAYS

13 JESUS CALLED TO PETER THE FISHERMAN

Jenny Dann (1952–)
arranged George F Bexon (1958–)

1. Jesus called to Peter the fisherman
   By the sea of Galilee;
   Jesus called to Peter the fisherman,
   'Leave your nets, come with me.'
   Jesus, you are calling me,
   Yes I can take your hand;
   Jesus, I will follow you
   Like Peter the fisherman.

2. Peter the fisherman followed Jesus
   By the sea of Galilee;
   Peter the fisherman followed Jesus
   When he said, 'Come with me.'
   Chorus

3. Peter became a people-fisherman,
   Everywhere God's love he shared;
   Peter became a people-fisherman,
   'Come to Jesus' he said.
   Chorus

4. Lord, send us out as people-fishermen,
   Everywhere your love to share;
   Lord, send us out as people-fishermen,
   Yours in action and prayer.
   Jesus, you are calling us,
   Yes we can take your hand;
   Jesus, we will follow you
   Like Peter the fisherman.

Jenny Dann (1952–)

Words and Music © 1995 Stainer & Bell Ltd and The Trustees for Methodist Church Purposes

Ask two children to mime the parts of Jesus and Peter as the song is sung. Include as many others as possible, in particular during the chorus, when they can follow Jesus and Peter. Everyone can join in on the last verse and chorus if the song is being performed by children to a congregation.

14 FOR GOD SO LOVED THE WORLD

Carol Rose (1955–)

1   For God so loved the world
    That he gave his only son
    That whosoever believes in him
        should live for ever;
    For God so loved the world
    That he gave his only son
    That whosoever believes in him
        should have eternal life.

2   God so loved us
    He sent Jesus;
    Jesus loves us,
    He's our Saviour.

Carol Rose (1955–)

Words and Music © 1995 Stainer & Bell Ltd and The Trustees for Methodist Church Purposes

A song for all ages. Divide into two groups, A and B. Group B begins as Group A begins verse 2. Alternatively, recorders, chime bars or other percussion can play the tune of the second verse as an accompaniment.

15 DAY BY DAY WITHOUT A WORD

June Baker (1936–)

Flowing

Day by day with-out a word The sky de-clares God's glo-ry! The sun, the moon and all the stars So quiet-ly tell the sto-ry. May the thoughts and words I say, Please you, God, as much to-day.

Day by day without a word
The sky declares God's glory!
The sun, the moon and all the stars
So quietly tell the story.
May the thoughts and words I say,
Please you, God, as much today.

Andrew E Pratt (1948–)
based on Psalm 19

Words and Music © 1995 Stainer & Bell Ltd and The Trustees for Methodist Church Purposes

A communal song which highlights the changing aspects of day and night. It can be sung as an accompaniment to slides of the beauty of creation or as a response to prayers of adoration. It could be the starting point of a creative workshop involving both children and adults.

16 WHEREVER YOU GO I WILL FOLLOW, FOLLOW, FOLLOW

June Baker (1936–)

1 Wherever you go I will follow, follow, follow,
Naomi, wherever you lead.
Wherever you go I will follow, follow, follow,
Naomi, wherever you lead.

2 Wherever you go I will follow, follow, follow,
Lord Jesus, wherever you lead.
Wherever you go I will follow, follow, follow,
Lord Jesus, wherever you lead.

Andrew E Pratt (1948–)

Words and Music © 1995 Stainer & Bell Ltd and The Trustees for Methodist Church Purposes

The first verse describes Ruth following Naomi, but other names may be inserted. The second verse links the call of the disciples with our own response to Jesus.

17 FOUR FRIENDS CARRY A NEIGHBOUR

*Traditional Sea Shanty
arranged Nicholas Williams (1959–)*

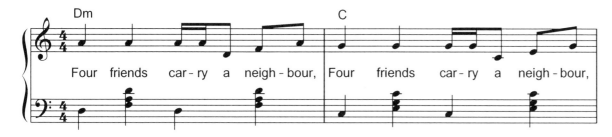

Four friends car-ry a neigh-bour, Four friends car-ry a neigh-bour,

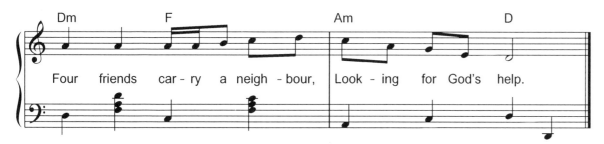

Four friends car-ry a neigh-bour, Look-ing for God's help.

Words and Arrangement © 1995 Stainer & Bell Ltd and The Trustees for Methodist Church Purposes

1 Four friends carry a neighbour,
Four friends carry a neighbour,
Four friends carry a neighbour,
Looking for God's help.

2 Can't get in, too many people, *(three times)*
Crowding round the door.

3 Up they go, climb to the rooftop, *(three times)*
Gently drop him in!

4 'Help our friend,' they call to Jesus, *(three times)*
'Help us if you can.'

5 Jesus smiles, makes him better, *(three times)*
'Take your bed and go.'

6 Hooray and up he rises! *(three times)*
Glory hallelujah!

Andrew E Pratt (1948–)

This is a 'fun' song, set to the tune of 'What shall we do with a drunken sailor?'. The last verse deliberately echoes this, while also using traditional words of praise. It works well enacted within a circle or acted out verse by verse with the words providing a commentary.

18 ONE DAY WHEN WE WERE FISHING

Peter Churchill (1963–)

Leader F / G7 / Bb / C

One day when we were fishing, On the lake so wide and deep, A storm blew up around us, But Jesus was a - sleep.

Everyone F C7 F / F C7 F

Oh the waves went in and the waves went out, And the

Gm / C / Gm / C

boat span round and round. Oh the rain came down and the

F A Dm / Bb F C7 / F

thun - der clapped, And we thought we would be drowned. **Children** Wake up Jesus! **Leader** But Jesus did not wake up.

Words and Music © Red Lentil Music from Feeling Good! published by The National Society. Used by permission.

Leader *(spoken)*
One day when we were fishing,
On the lake so wide and deep,
A storm blew up around us,
But Jesus was asleep.

Everyone *(singing, children in a circle, holding hands)*
Oh the waves went in and the waves went out, *(walk in
    and out)*
And the boat span round and round. *(turn round on the
    spot)*
Oh the rain came down and the thunder clapped, *(hand
    movements)*
And we thought we would be drowned.

Children *(shouting)*
Wake up Jesus!

Leader *(spoken)*
But Jesus did not wake up.

Everyone *(singing)*
Oh the waves went in...

Children *(shouting)*
Wake up Jesus!

Leader *(spoken)*
But Jesus still did not wake up.

Everyone *(singing)*
Oh the waves went in...

Children *(shouting)*
Wake up Jesus!

Leader *(spoken)*
And this time Jesus did wake up... and calmed the storm.

Everyone *(singing)*
Oh the waves were calm and the waves were still, *(stand still)*
And the boat stayed in one place.
Oh the rain dried up and the thunder stopped,
And we knew we would be safe.

Peter Churchill (1963–) and Sophie Churchill (1963–)

This dramatic song uses an adult leader for the spoken lines and a child to act the part of Jesus. Stand in a circle to perform this song and follow the simple movements as described. Ask one child to lie in the middle of the circle, pretending to be Jesus, asleep.

19 THE LORD, THE LORD

Traditional Melody
arranged Nicholas Williams (1959–)

1   The Lord, the Lord, the Lord is my shepherd,
The Lord, the Lord, the Lord is my shepherd,
The Lord, the Lord, the Lord is my shepherd,
The Lord is my shepherd and I shall not want.

2   He makes me lie down in green, green pastures,
He makes me lie down in green, green pastures,
He makes me lie down in green, green pastures,
The Lord is my shepherd and I shall not want.

3   He leads me beside the still, still waters.
He leads me beside the still, still waters.
He leads me beside the still, still waters.
The Lord is my shepherd and I shall not want.

Traditional based on Psalm 23

Arrangement © 1995 Stainer & Bell Ltd and The Trustees for Methodist Church Purposes

Known to adults, the words of this song are also accessible to children, including the very young. Ask an older child or adult to sing the first line of each verse and the rest of the group to echo it.

PEOPLE DAYS

20 GOD HAS GIVEN US EYES TO SEE

Traditional Ghanaian Melody

1 God has given us eyes to see, let's look!
God has given us eyes to see, let's look!
Let's look and see what is happening in the world around,
Let's look!
Let's look and see what is happening in the world around,
Let's look and see.

2 God has given us minds to think, let's pray!
God has given us minds to think, let's pray!
Let's pray and say, 'May your Kingdom come, your will
be done',
Let's pray!
Let's pray and say, 'May your Kingdom come, your will
be done',
Let's think and pray.

3 God has given us hands to use, let's work!
God has given us hands to use, let's work!
Let's work at things that need doing where we are today,
Let's work!
Let's work at things that need doing where we are today,
Let's work today!

4 God has given us feet to run, let's go!
God has given us feet to run, let's go!
Let's go and share all the love that God has given to us,
Let's go!
Let's go and share all the love that God has given to us,
Let's go God's way.

Peggy Ruddle (1919–)

Words © 1995 Stainer & Bell Ltd and The Trustees for Methodist Church Purposes

This song is a folk melody from Ghana. Use a drum on the first and third beat of each bar. Encourage everyone to clap where there are rests in the melody and to add their own actions.

21 JESUS I KNOW YOU LIVE

Marjorie Waine (1916–)
arranged George F Bexon (1958–)

With a swing

Je - sus I know you live, Je - sus I

know you live, Je - sus I know you live, You

live in me to - day. -day.

1   Jesus I know you live,
    Jesus I know you live,
    Jesus I know you live,
    You live in me today.

2   Jesus I know you care,
    Jesus I know you care,
    Jesus I know you care,
    You care for me always.

3   Jesus I know you love,
    Jesus I know you love,
    Jesus I know you love,
    I want to love you too.

Marjorie Waine (1916–)

Words and Music © 1995 Stainer & Bell Ltd and The Trustees for Methodist Church Purposes

This song links with many of the stories of Jesus and is suitable for Easter.

22 ROUND AND ROUND THE CIRCLE

Judith Franklin (1947–)
arranged June Baker (1936–)

1 Round and round the circle goes
  A line without an end,
  So many different people
  And each one I call my friend.

2 All skip round together
  United in a ring,
  Clap your hands and turn around
  And everybody sing:

3 Round and round the circle goes
  A line without an end,
  So many different people
  And each one I call my friend.

Judith Franklin (1947–)

Words and Music © 1995 Stainer & Bell Ltd and The Trustees for Methodist Church Purposes

Sing the song once. Then give everybody the chance to say hello to one another and link hands with different people before singing it again.

23 PLAYING, RUNNING, SKIPPING, JUMPING!

Joy Webb (1932–)

Bouncy, lilting speed

Play-ing, run-ning, skip-ping, jump-ing!

Su - per things to do___ And I like them best when I am

Do-ing them with you.___ And I like them best when I am Do-ing them with you.

1 Playing, running, skipping, jumping!
Super things to do
And I like them best when I am
Doing them with you.
And I like them best when I am
Doing them with you.

2 Walking, swinging, dancing, singing,
Happy things to do!
And I like it best when I can
Share these things with you.
And I like it best when I can
Share these things with you.

3 Reading, talking, thinking, praying,
Lovely things to do,
But they're really special when I'm
Sharing them with you.
But they're really special when I'm
Sharing them with you.

Joy Webb (1932–)

Words and Music © 1995 Stainer & Bell Ltd and The Trustees for Methodist Church Purposes

This is a chance for children to sing about their relationships with friends, either their own friends or Jesus as their friend. With very young children use only one verse at a time. Experiment with starting this song slowly and speeding up. Encourage the children to invent and perform their own actions.

24 KEEP A LIGHT IN YOUR EYES

Ruth Thomas (1956–)

Words and Music © 1995 Stainer & Bell Ltd and The Trustees for Methodist Church Purposes

1   Keep a light in your eyes for the children of the world
    For the children of the world, for the children.
    Keep a light in your eyes for the children of the world
    For the children of the world need you.
    Keep a candle burning, burning, burning,
    Keep a candle burning, burning, burning,
    Keep a candle burning, burning, burning,
    For the children of the world.

2   Keep strength in your heart for the children of the world
    For the children of the world, for the children.
    Keep strength in your heart for the children of the world
    For the children of the world need you.
    Chorus

3   Keep a song on your lips for the children of the world
    For the children of the world, for the children.
    Keep a song on your lips for the children of the world
    For the children of the world need you.
    Chorus

4   Light a candle in the minds of the children of the world
    Of the children of the world, of the children.
    Light a candle in the minds of the children of the world
    For the children of the world need you.
    Chorus

Ruth Thomas (1956–)

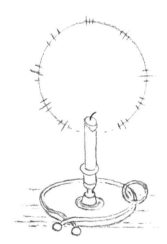

This song can be linked to prayers for children in other countries, and can be used at baptism or at times of loss.

25 DUW SY'N DY GARU DI
YOU ARE LOVED BY GOD

Jim Clarke (1954–)
arranged Nicholas Williams (1959–)

Duw sy'n dy garu di (enw);
Duw sy'n dy garu di.
Teimlaf wres ei gariad Ef
Yn dy gynnal di bob awr.

Jim Clarke (1954–)

You are loved by God (name);
You are loved by God.
Feel the warmth of God's pure love
And his caring for you each day.

English Translation Delyth Wyn (1961–)

Words and Music © 1995 Stainer & Bell Ltd and The Trustees for Methodist Church Purposes

Make sure that no-one is left out when this song is sung by a small group . In a larger group people sing to those on each side of them or choose a partner to sing to. Remember that adults also need to feel affirmed.

26 WHO MADE YOUR EYES?

Lillian Waldecker

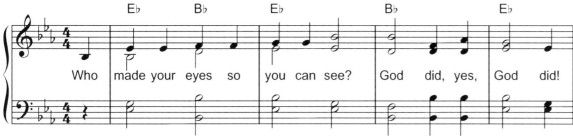

Who made your eyes so you can see? God did, yes, God did!

1   Who made your eyes so you can see?
    God did, yes, God did!

2   Who made your ears so you can hear?
    God did, yes, God did!

3   Who made your tongue so you can speak?
    God did, yes, God did!

4   Who made your hands so you can work?
    God did, yes, God did!

5   Who made your feet so you can walk?
    God did, yes, God did!

Lillian Waldecker

Words and Music © 1978 Scripture Press Publications, Inc. All rights reserved. Used by permission.

This is a song for very young children. Point to the appropriate part of the body for each verse. At the words 'God did', everyone spreads their arms out widely to imply that God is all around us and we are held in God's arms.

27   I LOVE YOU LORD JESUS

Paul Crouch (1963–) and David Mudie (1961–)

Words and Music © 1989 Daybreak Music Ltd, 4 Regency Mews, Silverdale Road, Eastbourne, BN20 7AB. Used by permission.

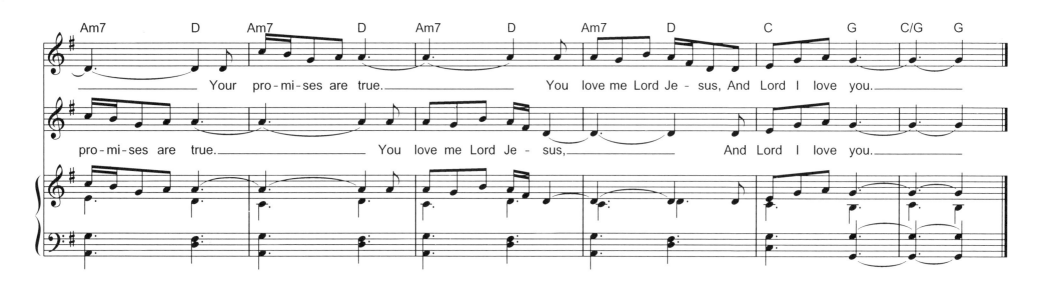

Your pro-mi-ses are true. You love me Lord Je - sus, And Lord I love you.

pro-mi-ses are true. You love me Lord Je - sus, And Lord I love you.

I love you Lord Jesus
The King of all things.
You love me Lord Jesus,
Your love never ends.
To you I am special,
Your promises are true.
You love me Lord Jesus,
And Lord I love you.

Paul Crouch (1963–) and David Mudie (1961–)

Sing this song either with a leader taking one part and the group the other, or with the parts shared equally between two groups. An echo may arise naturally on the last phrase. Let it happen anyway!

28 GOOD MORNING, JESUS

Estelle White (1925–)

1 Good morning, Jesus,
   Good morning, Lord,
   Good morning, Jesus,
   Good morning, Lord,
   Good morning, Jesus,
   Good morning, Lord,
   And I thank you for another day.

2 I'm glad you're with me,
   I'm glad you're here,
   I'm glad you're with me,
   I'm glad you're here,
   I'm glad you're with me,
   I'm glad you're here,
   And I thank you for another day.

3 Good morning, Jesus,
   Good morning, Lord,
   Good morning, Jesus,
   Good morning, Lord,
   Good morning, Jesus,
   Good morning, Lord,
   And I thank you for another day.

Estelle White (1925–)

Words and Music © 1977 Kevin Mayhew Ltd. Used by permission from *Good Morning, Jesus*, Licence No. 498051.

This song is ideally suited to singing at the beginning of the day.

CHRISTMAS DAYS

29 COME, LORD JESUS, COME

Francesca Leftley (1955–)

1 Come, Lord Jesus, come.
  Come, Lord Jesus, come.
  Come, Lord Jesus, come,
  To this world of ours.

2 Lord, we need you now;
  Lord, we need you now;
  Lord we need you now
  In this world of ours.

3 Fill us with your peace;
  Fill us with your peace;
  Fill us with your peace
  In this world of ours.

4 Touch us with your love;
  Touch us with your love;
  Touch us with your love
  In this world of ours.

5 May we see your light;
  May we see your light;
  May we see your light
  In this world of ours.

Francesca Leftley (1955–)

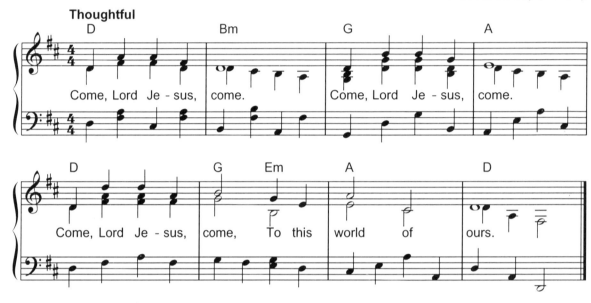

OPTIONAL DESCANT

Words and Music © 1986 Kevin Mayhew Ltd. Used by permission from *Many Ways to Praise*, Licence No. 498051.

This song is particularly suitable for Advent, when children could make a frieze showing the Advent journey. It can also be used as a response during prayers. The optional descant played on chime bars would give an added seasonal flavour to the song.

30 WHO CAME TO MARY?

Judith Franklin (1947–)
arranged June Baker (1936–)

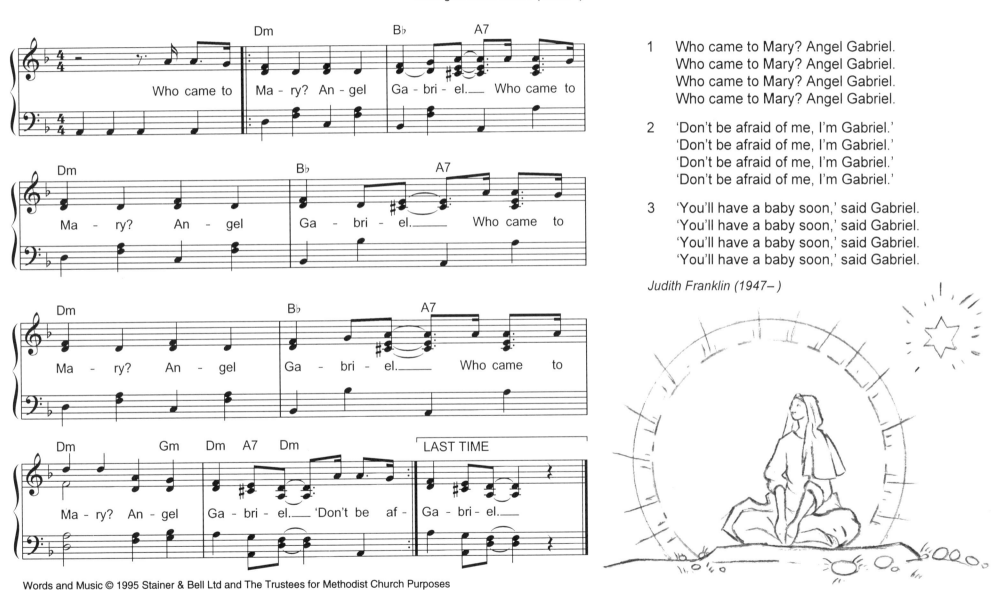

1   Who came to Mary? Angel Gabriel.
    Who came to Mary? Angel Gabriel.
    Who came to Mary? Angel Gabriel.
    Who came to Mary? Angel Gabriel.

2   'Don't be afraid of me, I'm Gabriel.'
    'Don't be afraid of me, I'm Gabriel.'
    'Don't be afraid of me, I'm Gabriel.'
    'Don't be afraid of me, I'm Gabriel.'

3   'You'll have a baby soon,' said Gabriel.
    'You'll have a baby soon,' said Gabriel.
    'You'll have a baby soon,' said Gabriel.
    'You'll have a baby soon,' said Gabriel.

Judith Franklin (1947–)

Words and Music © 1995 Stainer & Bell Ltd and The Trustees for Methodist Church Purposes

In addition to singing, children may clap or play unpitched percussion during this song. An older child can sing the first line of each verse, copied by the others.

31 SLEEP, SLEEP, GENTLY SLEEP

Judith Franklin (1947–)
arranged June Baker (1936–)

Sleep, sleep, gently sleep,
Close your eyes, you're cradled in
    the arms of Mary,
Sleep, sleep, gently sleep,
In the arms of Mary.

Judith Franklin (1947–)

Words and Music © 1995 Stainer & Bell Ltd and The Trustees for Methodist Church Purposes

A very quiet song for young children, who can make gentle cradling movements as they sing.

32 'TWEET, TWEET, TWEET,' SAID THE ROBIN

Susan Burman (1940–)

1   'Tweet, tweet, tweet,' said the robin,
    'Baa, baa, baa,' said the lamb.
    'Moo, moo, moo,' said the old brown cow
    In the stable in Bethlehem.

2   'What is that?' said the robin,
    'I don't know,' said the lamb.
    'It's a tiny little baby,' said the old brown cow,
    In the stable in Bethlehem.

3   Stars shine down on the robin.
    Stars shine down on the lamb.
    Stars shine down on the tiny little baby
    In the stable in Bethlehem.

Susan Burman (1940–)

Words and Music © 1995 Stainer & Bell Ltd and The Trustees for Methodist Church Purposes

To dramatise this song the children could either play the parts of the animals or make animal masks on sticks.

33 NOEL, NOEL, NOEL

Joy Webb (1932–)

Words and Music © Salvationist Publishing and Supplies Ltd. Used by permission.

Noel, Noel, Noel... (sing eight 'Noels' with nine echoes)

1   If I were a star then I would shine, shine, shine;
     The brightest light in heaven would be mine, mine, mine;
     So all the world would know that it is Christmas time,
     I would shine, shine, shine.

2   If I were a candle I would glow, glow, glow;
     My pretty light would help the world to know, know, know
     That long ago a baby came God's love to show,
     I would glow, glow, glow.

3   I am just a child but I can sing, sing, sing;
     I can make the world with happy music ring,
     Sing about the peace the holy child can bring,
     I can sing, sing, sing.

Joy Webb (1932–)

Lively group singing in this carol is best encouraged by dividing the singers into two groups (perhaps children echoed by adults) for the 'Noels' which make up the chorus. Ask one child or several children to sing the verses.

34   WE TEND OUR SHEEP

Valerie Ruddle (1932–)

1   We tend our sheep, we tend our sheep
    Upon the hillside green. *(twice)*

2   We build a fire, we build a fire
    To keep the wolves away. *(twice)*

3   We cook our food, we cook our food;
    We're very hungry now. *(twice)*

4   We dance and sing, we dance and sing
    To keep us warm tonight. *(twice)*

5   We play our pipes, we play our pipes
    To keep ourselves awake. *(twice)*

6   Let's hurry now, let's hurry now;
    To Bethlehem we go. *(twice)*

Valerie Ruddle (1932–)

Words and Music © 1995 Stainer & Bell Ltd and The Trustees for Methodist Church Purposes

This is a song with an obvious relevance to the Christmas season and — with the last verse omitted — to other times of the year. Other verses can be added to connect it with, for example, the story of the lost sheep.

35 AR FORE DYDD NADOLIG
'TWAS EARLY CHRISTMAS MORNING

Arfon Wyn (1952–)

(G) Ar fo - re dydd Nad - o - lig, Ar
'Twas ear - ly Christ - mas morn - ing, 'Twas

(Am) (D7) (G) fo - re dydd Na - do - lig, Ar fo - re dydd Na -
ear - ly Christ - mas morn - ing, 'Twas ear - ly Christ - mas

(C) (D) (C) (G) -do - lig, Fe an - wyd Crist i'r byd.
morn - ing, That Christ was born on earth.

DESCANT

Ar fore dydd Nadolig,
Ar fore dydd Nadolig,
Ar fore dydd Nadolig,
Fe anwyd Crist i'r byd.

1 Fe welais y bugeiliaid, *(three times)*
   Yn gwylio'u defaid man.
   Cytgan

2 Fe welais i y doethion, *(three times)*
   Yn dod o'r dwyrain pell.
   Cytgan

3 Awn ninnau i'w addoli, *(three times)*
   Y Brenin ddaeth o'r Nef.
   Cytgan

Arfon Wyn (1952–)

'Twas early Christmas morning,
'Twas early Christmas morning,
'Twas early Christmas morning,
That Christ was born on earth.

1 I saw the shepherds watching, *(three times)*
   They watched their sheep with care.
   Chorus

2 I saw the wise men trav'lling, *(three times)*
   They travelled from the East.
   Chorus

3 Now let us also worship, *(three times)*
   The King who came to earth.
   Chorus

English Translation Delyth Wyn (1961–)

Words and Music © Cyhoeddiadau Curiad

Sing the song while nativity figures made by the children are put in place. Ask one or more children to sing the first line of each verse for the others to copy.

36 GANWYD CRIST YM METHLEHEM
CHRIST WAS BORN IN BETHLEHEM

Arfon Wyn (1952–)

Gan - wyd Crist ym Meth - le - 'em,
Christ was born in Beth - le - hem,

Gan - wyd Crist ym Meth - le - 'em,
Christ was born in Beth - le - hem,

Gan - wyd Crist ym Meth - le - 'em, Ym
Christ was born in Beth - le - hem, In

Meth - le - hem___ Jiw - dea.___
Beth - le - hem___ Ju - dea. ___

Can - wch Ha - le - liw - ia
Praise Him Hal - le - lu - jah

Can - wch Ha - le - liw - ia
Praise Him Hal - le - lu - jah

Can - wch Ha - le - liw - ia
Praise Him Hal - le - lu - jah

Can - wch glod___ i Dduw.
Sing our praise___ to God.

Words and Music © Cyhoeddiadau Curiad

1   Ganwyd Crist ym Methle'em,
Ganwyd Crist ym Methle'em,
Ganwyd Crist ym Methle'em,
Ym Methlehem Jiwdea.
Canwch Haleliwia
Canwch Haleliwia
Canwch Haleliwia
Canwch glod i Dduw.

2   Seren yn disgleirio,
Seren yn disgleirio,
Seren yn disgleirio,
Disgleirio yn y nos.
Cytgan

3   Canu mae angylion,
Canu mae angylion,
Canu mae angylion,
Gogoniant iddo Ef.
Cytgan

4   Doethion a bugeiliaid ddaethant,
Doethion a bugeiliaid ddaethant,
Doethion a bugeiliaid ddaethant,
I'w addoli Ef.
Cytgan

Arfon Wyn (1952–)

1   Christ was born in Bethlehem,
Christ was born in Bethlehem,
Christ was born in Bethlehem,
In Bethlehem Judea.
Praise Him Hallelujah
Praise Him Hallelujah
Praise Him Hallelujah
Sing our praise to God.

2   See the brightly shining star,
See the brightly shining star,
See the brightly shining star,
Shining in the night.
Chorus

3   Hear the choir of angels sing,
Hear the choir of angels sing,
Hear the choir of angels sing,
Glory to our God.
Chorus

4   Shepherds and the wise men came,
Shepherds and the wise men came,
Shepherds and the wise men came,
Came to worship Him.
Chorus

English Translation Delyth Wyn (1961–)

This is an original Welsh song with a Caribbean flavour. If possible it could to be accompanied by bongos, maracas and other West Indian instruments. Encourage the children to find out what sounds they can make using rubber top sticks, a metal dustbin lid, and even the base of a dustbin!

37 A SPECIAL STAR

Lynda Masson (1951–)

1 A special star, a special star
It led the way to Jesus.
A special star, a special star
Shone over where he lay.

2 A special star, a special star
It led three Kings to Jesus.
A special star, a special star
Led Kings to worship him.

3 A special star, a special star
Shone over baby Jesus
A special star, a special star
Leads us to worship him.

Lynda Masson (1951–)

Words and Music © 1995 Stainer & Bell Ltd and The Trustees for Methodist Church Purposes

Encourage some of the children to make a large silver star, which should be fastened to a stick. One child can then hold it up high, moving around while the others follow, singing the song. At the end of the song everyone kneels round the star.

EASTER DAYS

38 HOSANNA, HOSANNA

Arfon Wyn (1952–)

1 Hosanna, Hosanna,
Galwn Iesu, arnat Ti;
Ti yw'n cyfaill, Ti yw'n Brenin,
Rhoddwn groeso mawr i Ti.

2 O ein Iesu, O ein Iesu,
Diolch Iesu, diolch i Ti;
Ti yw'n cyfaill, Ti yw'n Brenin,
Buost farw drosom ni.

3 Haleliwia, Haleliwia,
Canwn, Iesu, 'rwyt yn fyw;
Ti yw'n cyfaill, Ti yw'n Brenin,
Llawenhawn a molwn Di.

Arfon Wyn (1952–)

1 Hosanna, Hosanna,
Shout to Jesus as he comes;
He is special, he is special,
Shout Hosanna to the King.

2 He is dying, he is dying,
Cry for Jesus on the cross;
He was special, he was special,
He is dying, God's own son.

3 Alleluia, Alleluia,
Sing to Jesus, he's alive;
He is special, he is special,
Alleluia to the Lord.

Arfon Wyn (1952–)

Words and Music © Cyhoeddiadau Curiad

The first verse of this song can be sung on Palm Sunday, adding the other verses on Good Friday and Easter Sunday. The second verse should be sung very slowly and sadly.

39 CHRIST IS COMING

Aileen Robertson

1   'Christ is coming, Christ is coming,
     On a donkey, on a donkey,
     Hosanna, Hosanna,
     We wave our palm branches.'

Lothian Road Church Primary School, Edinburgh.

2   'Christ is risen, Christ is risen,
     Hallelujah! Hallelujah!
     He is with us, He is with us,
     Today and for ever.'

Cynthia Dean

Words and Music © The Church of Scotland/St Andrew's Press. Used by permission from *The Church Nursery Group.*

Sing the first verse on Palm Sunday, waving branches made by the children. Use the second verse on Easter Day, throwing arms up in delight.

40   TWO LONG PIECES OF WOOD

June Baker (1936–)

1   Two long pieces of wood,
    Nailed together make a cross,
    Far away in Jerusalem,
    That's the way it was.

2   Three tall crosses of wood,
    Stand together on a hill,
    Far away in Jerusalem
    That's the way it was.

3   Sadly hanging on cross of wood,
    Jesus stretches his arms out wide,
    Far away in Jerusalem—
    That's the way it was.

4   Empty cross and empty grave
    Far away in Jerusalem
    God has shown us a heart of love—
    That's the way it was,
    That's the way it is!

June Baker (1936–)

Words and Music © 1995 Stainer & Bell Ltd and The Trustees for Methodist Church Purposes

Sing the first three verses softly and sadly, making a clear contrast with the fourth verse which should be happy, and louder, accompanied by big smiles!

41 EASTER TELLS US

J P McDonald

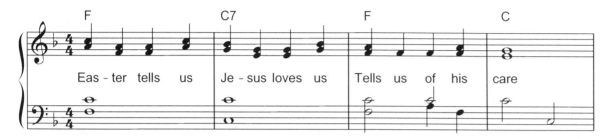

Eas - ter tells us   Je - sus loves us   Tells us of his   care

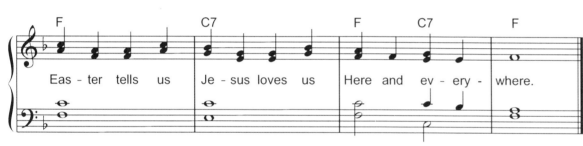

Eas - ter tells us   Je - sus loves us   Here and ev - ery - where.

Easter tells us
Jesus loves us
Tells us of his care
Easter tells us
Jesus loves us
Here and everywhere.

J P McDonald

Words and Music © The Church of Scotland/St Andrew's Press. Used by permission from *The Church Nursery Group.*

Make an Easter garden together using natural materials (plus artificial flowers if necessary) or plasticine, paper, card etc. Sing the song as you move the stone away from the tomb.

42 ALLELUIA, ALLELUIA, WINTER HAS FLED

Estelle White (1925–)

1 Alleluia, alleluia,
Winter has fled and the days grow longer,
Alleluia, alleluia,
Jesus is risen and he's here!

2 Alleluia, alleluia,
Springtime is here and the buds are green,
Alleluia, alleluia,
Jesus is risen and he's here!

3 Alleluia, alleluia,
Out in the fields there are skipping lambs,
Alleluia, alleluia,
Jesus is risen and he's here!

Estelle White (1925–)

Words and Music © 1977 Kevin Mayhew Ltd. Used by permission from *Good Morning, Jesus,* Licence No. 498051

A song for Easter to Pentecost. Have different signs of spring for the children to look at each week. Encourage them to find their own. They may want to add new words to the song to express the joy of springtime.

43 ALLELUIA (SOUTH AFRICA)

*Traditional South African Melody
transcribed from singing of George Mxadana*

Warm and purposefully

Alleluia. Alleluia.
Alleluia. Alleluia.
Alleluia. Alleluia.
Alleluia. Alleluia.

Traditional Liturgical Text

Arrangement © 1991 Wild Goose Resource Group, Iona Community, Glasgow, Scotland. Used by permission of GIA Publications Inc, Chicago, Illinois, exclusive agents for USA and Canada and of the Iona Community for the rest of the world.

Use this song as a response to prayer or as a song to sing during Holy Communion while the Peace is shared. It can be sung getting louder and louder or softer and softer, depending on the circumstances.

44 HAPPY EASTER WE WILL SAY

Anonymous
arranged Nicholas Williams (1959–)

Arrangement © 1995 Stainer & Bell Ltd and The Trustees for Methodist Church Purposes

'Happy Easter' we will say,
Our Lord Jesus lives today!

Anonymous

An Easter greeting song which can be repeated several times.

FESTIVAL DAYS

45 MAY YOUR LOVING SPIRIT

Melody from manuscript (1756) noted by
W H Gratton Flood (1859–1928)
arranged June Baker (1936–)

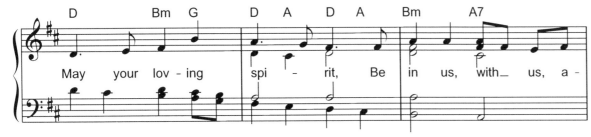

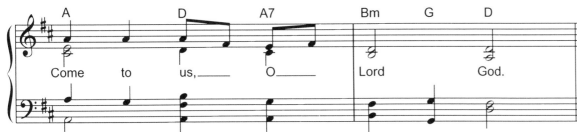

1 May your loving spirit,
  Be in us, with us, around us,
  May your loving spirit,
  Come to us, O Lord God.

2 May your loving spirit,
  Surround us, shield us, shelter us,
  May your loving spirit,
  Come to us, O Lord God.

3 May your loving spirit,
  Hold us, help us, heal us,
  May your loving spirit,
  Come to us, O Lord God.

June Baker (1936–)

Words and Arrangement © 1995 Stainer & Bell Ltd and The Trustees for Methodist Church Purposes

This song, set to a beautiful Irish tune, may be used to celebrate Pentecost, as a response to prayer, or as preparation for worship.

46 GOD HAS PUT A CIRCLE ROUND US

Jenny Dann (1952–)
arranged Nicholas Williams (1959–)

1 God has put a circle round us
   Up and down and all around us
   God has put a circle round us
   Thank you, Lord.

2 Jesus came into the circle
   Right in the middle of the circle
   Jesus came into the circle
   Thank you, Lord.

3 Jesus shows how much God loves us
   Now and always, yes he loves us
   Jesus shows how much God loves us
   Thank you, Lord.

4 God has put a circle round us
   By his Spirit all around us
   God has put a circle round us
   Thank you, Lord.

Jenny Dann (1952–)

Words and Music © 1995 Stainer & Bell Ltd and The Trustees for Methodist Church Purposes

A song which is useful at any time of the year, but is particularly appropriate to Pentecost. Make up simple actions, following the words, or invent a dance, asking for a volunteer to play the part of Jesus.

47 O WHAT A WONDERFUL WORLD

Estelle White (1925–)

1   O what a wonderful world!
    O what a wonderful world it is!
    O what a wonderful world!
    Thank you, heav'nly Father.

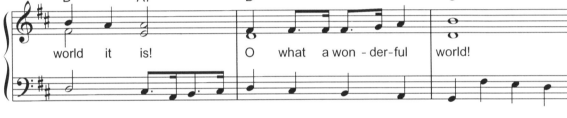

2   O what a beautiful world!
    O what a beautiful world it is!
    O what a beautiful world!
    Thank you, my Lord Jesus.

3   O what a marvellous world!
    O what a marvellous world it is!
    O what a marvellous world!
    Thank you, Holy Spirit.

Estelle White (1925–)

Words and Music © 1977 Kevin Mayhew Ltd. Used by permission from *Good Morning, Jesus*, Licence No. 498051.

This Pentecost song can also be sung at any time of the year by all ages, including the very young.

48   I AM THE CHURCH

Richard Avery (1934–)
and Donald Marsh (1923–)

I am the church! (Point to yourself with your thumb)
You are the church! (Point to your partner)
We are the church together! (Shake hands)
All who follow Jesus, (Reach out both hands)
All around the world. (Circle arms over head)
Yes, we're the church together. (Link arms)

1   The church is not a building, the church is not
       a steeple,
    The church is not a resting place, the church is
       a people!
    Chorus

2   We're many kinds of people, with many kinds
       of faces:
    All colours and all ages too, from all kinds
       of places.
    Chorus

Richard Avery (1934–) and Donald Marsh (1923–)

Words and Music © 1972 by Hope Publishing Co, Carol Stream, Il 60188. All rights reserved. Used by permission.

This is a song for Pentecost, Church Anniversaries, Saints' Days and for more general use.

49 GLORY TO GOD

Source unknown,
probably Peruvian

Leader	Glory to God, Glory to God Glory to the Father.
Everyone	Glory to God, glory to God Glory to the Father.
Leader	To God be glory for ever.
Everyone	To God be glory for ever.
Leader	Alleluia, Amen.
Everyone	Alleluia, Amen.
Divide in 2	Alleluia, Amen.
Divide in 3	Alleluia, Amen.
Leader	Glory to God, Glory to God Glory to Christ Jesus.
Everyone	Glory to God, glory to God Glory to Christ Jesus.
Leader	To God be glory for ever.
Everyone	To God be glory for ever. Alleluia...
Leader	Glory to God, Glory to God Glory to the Spirit.
Everyone	Glory to God, glory to God Glory to God the Spirit.
Leader	To God be glory for ever.
Everyone	To God be glory for ever. Alleluia....

This Gloria probably comes from Peru, and should be sung unaccompanied by a leader and three groups. It is ideal for Pentecost or for use in a service of Holy Communion.

50 MIS MAWRTH UNWAITH ETO
MARCH THE FIRST IS HERE AGAIN

Ceri Gwyn (1964–)

Words and Music © 1995 Stainer & Bell Ltd and The Trustees for Methodist Church Purposes

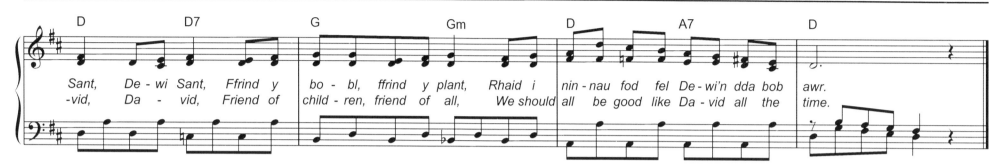

Sant, De - wi Sant, Ffrind y | bo - bl, ffrind y plant, Rhaid i | nin - nau fod fel De - wi'n dda bob | awr.
-vid, Da - vid, Friend of | child - ren, friend of all, We should | all be good like Da - vid all the | time.

Mis Mawrth unwaith eto
A'r gwanwyn wedi dod;
Dydd Gŵyl Dewi ydyw hi.
Mis Mawrth unwaith eto
A'r gwanwyn wedi dod;
Dydd Gŵyl Dewi ydyw hi.
Dewi Sant, Dewi Sant, cofiwn Dewi,
Cofiwn am y pethau bach a'r pethau mawr,
Dewi Sant, Dewi Sant,
Ffrind y bobl, ffrind y plant,
Rhaid i ninnau fod fel Dewi'n dda bob awr.

March the first is here again
And we will celebrate;
Celebrate Saint David's Day.
March the first is here again
And we will celebrate;
Celebrate Saint David's Day.
David, David, we remember,
All the small things and the great things that he did.
David, David,
Friend of children, friend of all,
We should all be good like David all the time.

Ceri Gwyn (1964–)

English Translation Delyth Wyn (1961–)

St Patrick's Day
It is March the seventeenth
And we will celebrate;
Celebrate Saint Patrick's Day.
It is March the seventeenth
And we will celebrate;
Celebrate Saint Patrick's Day.
Patrick, Patrick, we remember,
That he helped to spread God's love
*   throughout the land.*
Patrick, Patrick, friend of Ireland, friend of all,
We should all work very hard to share
*   God's love.*

St George's Day
April twenty-third is here
And we will celebrate;
Celebrate Saint George's Day.
April twenty-third is here
And we will celebrate;
Celebrate Saint George's Day.
Saint George, Saint George, we remember
He fought bravely 'gainst the evil in the land.
Saint George, Saint George, friend of people,
*   friend of God,*
We should all be brave and conquer bad with
*   good.*

St Andrew's Day
Last day of November,
And we will celebrate;
Celebrate Saint Andrew's Day.
Last day of November,
And we will celebrate;
Celebrate Saint Andrew's Day.
Andrew, Andrew, we remember,
Jesus told him 'Go and fish for people now'
Andrew, Andrew, friend of Jesus, friend of
*   all,*
We should also try to share God's love with
*   all.*

Additional Verses by Delyth Wyn (1961–)

This song, written originally to celebrate Saint David's Day, now has verses to celebrate the patron saints of England, Scotland and Ireland.

51 FIRST THE SEED AND THEN THE RAIN

Traditional
arranged Nicholas Williams (1959–)

1   First the seed and then the rain
     Alleluia
     Then the sun to swell the grain
     Alleluia.

2   Soon the green shoots spring to birth
     Alleluia
     Breaking through the sleeping earth
     Alleluia.

3   Look the warm sun fills the ear
     Alleluia
     As the harvest time draws near
     Alleluia.

4   All the richness of the field
     Alleluia
     Now its fruitful corn to yield
     Alleluia.

5   Praise to God who gives us bread
     Alleluia
     That his world may all be fed
     Alleluia.

Ivy Calvert (1922–) and Janet Cumming (1938–)

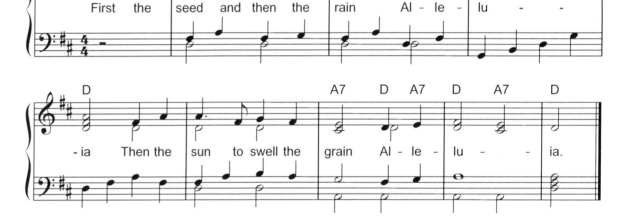

First the seed and then the rain Al-le-lu - - -ia Then the sun to swell the grain Al-le-lu - - ia.

Words and Arrangement © 1995 Stainer & Bell Ltd and The Trustees for Methodist Church Purposes

A harvest song for all ages. Encourage the very young children to join in the 'alleluias' with great enthusiasm.

52   GOD, YOU HOLD ME

George F Bexon (1958–)

1   God, you hold me, like a mother,
Safely on her knee;
God, you hold me, like a mother,
Close to you but free.

2   God, you watch me when I wander,
Keep me in your sight.
God, you watch me when I wander,
Hold me day and night.

3   God, you hold me, like a mother,
Teach me to be free,
God, you hold me, like a mother,
Show your love to me.

Andrew E Pratt (1948–)

Words and Music © 1995 Stainer & Bell Ltd and The Trustees for Methodist Church Purposes

A quiet prayer intended for Mothering Sunday, but with opportunities for use in many other situations.

53 WE THANK YOU GOD FOR MUMMIES

Judy Jarvis (1940–)
arranged June Baker (1936–)

1 We thank you God for mummies, (mothers, mums)
   (three times)
Today and every day.

and/or

For mummy's love and cuddles, *(three times)*
Today and every day.

2 We thank you God for daddies, (fathers, dads)
   (three times)
Today and every day.

and/or

For daddy's fun and kindness, *(three times)*
Today and every day.

3 We thank you God for sisters,
For silly, spiteful sisters, *(twice)*
Today and every day.

and

We thank you God for sisters,
For sharing, caring sisters, *(twice)*
Today and every day.

4 We thank you God for brothers,
For bossy, boastful brothers, *(twice)*
Today and every day.

and

We thank you God for brothers,
For gentle, helpful brothers, *(twice)*
Today and every day.

5 We thank you God for babies,
For tiny crying babies, *(twice)*
Today and every day.

Judy Jarvis (1940–)

Words and Music © 1995 Stainer & Bell Ltd and The Trustees for Methodist Church Purposes

Requests for a very simple Mothering Sunday song for Under Fives inspired the composition of this song. Choose whichever group of verses is appropriate, and invent some of your own.

SPECIAL DAYS

54 *GLORY TO OUR WONDERFUL GOD*

Jenny Dann (1952–)

Lively and joyful

Glo - ry to our won - der - ful God, Won - der - ful God, Oh,

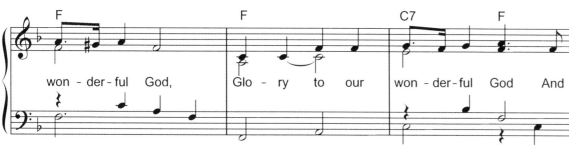

won - der - ful God, Glo - ry to our won - der - ful God And

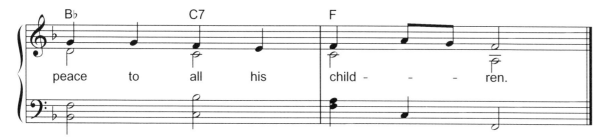

peace to all his child - - - ren.

Glory to our wonderful God,
Wonderful God,
Oh, wonderful God,
Glory to our wonderful God
And peace to all his children.

Jenny Dann (1952–)

Words and Music © 1995 Stainer & Bell Ltd and The Trustees for Methodist Church Purposes

Use this song, repeated several times, in the service of Holy Communion, or for the beginning or end of the day.

55 FROM HAND TO HAND

Andrew Eaton (1966–)
arranged Nicholas Williams (1959–)

1 From hand to hand, from hand to hand
We pass the Bread of Life.
From heart to heart, from heart to heart,
We pass the bread with love.

2 From hand to hand, from hand to hand
We pass the cup of wine,
From heart to heart, from heart to heart
We pass the cup with love.

Andrew Eaton (1966–)

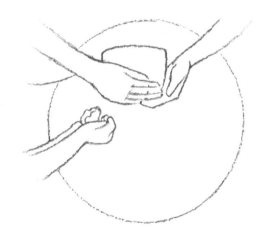

Words and Music © 1995 Stainer & Bell Ltd and The Trustees for Methodist Church Purposes

This gentle song is for people of all ages to sing as they share in Holy Communion. Sing it in two groups, the first taking the main tune, the second entering with the ostinato harmony after the song has been sung once.

56 HERE'S A PARTY

June Baker (1936–)

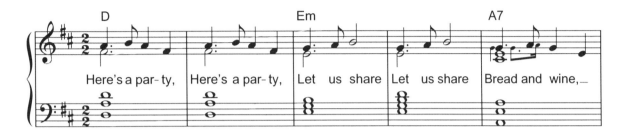

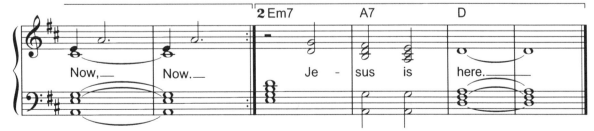

1 Here's a party (table),
Let us share
Bread and wine,
With Jesus here,
Gather round
Come to the feast,
Now, now.

2 Come the greatest
And the least,
Come to the party (table)
Here we share;
Come to the party (table),
Jesus is here.

Andrew E Pratt (1948–)

Words and Music © 1995 Stainer & Bell Ltd and The Trustees for Methodist Church Purposes

Use this song for Holy Communion, singing it in two groups echoing each other or with leader and response. 'Table' may be substituted for 'party' throughout the song.

57 THE PEACE OF THE LORD

Brian Hoare (1935–)

The Peace of the Lord be always with you,
I greet you in his name.
The Peace of the Lord be always with you,
I greet you in his name.

Brian Hoare (1935–)

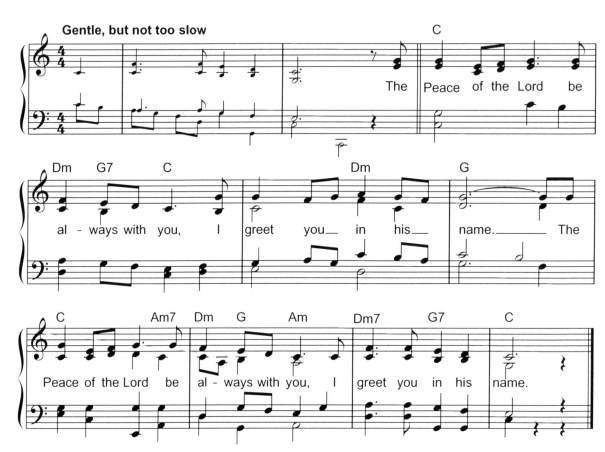

Words and Music © Brian Hoare/Jubilate Hymns for world excluding USA and Canada. © Hope Publishing Company, Carol Stream, IL 60188 for USA and Canada.

Sing the song over and over again to share the Peace or to greet each other.

58   THE LOVE OF GOD

Sylvia Crowther (1946–)

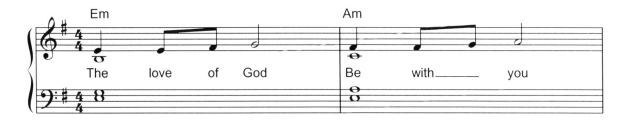

The love of God   Be with_____ you

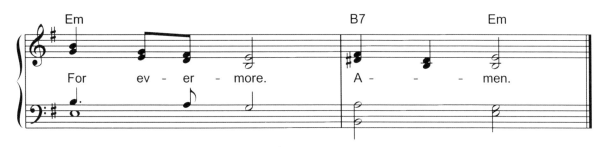

For ev - er - more.   A - - men.

The love of God
Be with you
For evermore.
Amen.

Traditional

Music © 1995 Stainer & Bell Ltd and The Trustees for Methodist Church Purposes

Actions (Sylvia Crowther)

1st line:	Touch right hand on left shoulder and stretch out.
2nd line:	Touch left hand on right shoulder and stretch out.
3rd line:	Bring hands together, palms up, into the body.
4th line:	Place hands in prayer position.

This song can replace or come after the Benediction at the end of a service or session. It would be particularly suitable to follow a Baptism or Dedication. If the actions are used they should be done slowly and reverently. Don't attempt them if the children are likely to giggle! Very young children should try a simpler version with, perhaps, two actions.

59 WELCOME, WELCOME, TODAY

June Baker (1936–)

1 Welcome, welcome, today, welcome
   to our family,
   Welcome, welcome, today, we all pray
   and welcome you.

2 Welcome, welcome, today, welcome
   to our family,
   Welcome, welcome, today, we all love
   and welcome you.

3 Welcome, welcome, today, welcome
   to our family,
   Welcome, welcome, today, we are
   all God's family.

June Baker (1936–)

Words and Music © 1995 Stainer & Bell Ltd and The Trustees for Methodist Church Purposes

This song can be used following a Baptism, Dedication or Confirmation. It can also be used to welcome a new child to a group.

60 TINGLE, TINGLE, TINGLE

June Baker (1936–)

Tingle, tingle, tingle with excitement!
Laugh, laugh, laugh until you ache!
Wondering, wondering,
What difference another day will make;
But this day is your birthday,
You're bigger, bigger, bigger, now by far!
We all thank God for making you
The special, special person that you are!

Andrew E Pratt (1948–)

Words and Music © 1995 Stainer & Bell Ltd and The Trustees for Methodist Church Purposes

Ask the child celebrating the birthday to crouch down until the sixth line and then to get bigger and bigger before standing on tiptoes and raising arms in the air. Sing the song again, letting everybody crouch and then grow.

61 IT'S BIRTHDAY TIME

Peter Churchill (1963–)

It's birthday time for (Rachel),
Three cheers, hip, hip, hooray!
We ask God to be with (her)
As (she) grows day by day.
We start our lives curled up so small
And every year we grow,
And soon we stand as tall as trees,
Stretched out from top to toe.
(Repeat first four lines).

Peter Churchill (1963–) and Sophie Churchill (1963–)

Words and Music © Red Lentil Music from *Feeling Good!* published by The National Society. Used by permission.

In this birthday song the children crouch down on the fifth line and gradually make themselves bigger as they sing.

CREATION DAYS

62 BIG BLUE PLANET

June Baker (1936–)

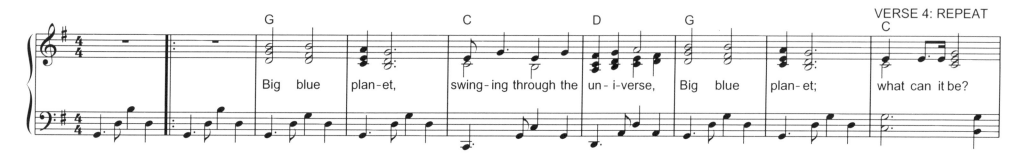

Big blue plan-et, swing-ing through the un-i-verse, Big blue plan-et; what can it be?

what can it be? It's the plan-et earth, it's the plan-et earth. It's the plan-et earth, it's the plan-et earth. Big blue plan-et,

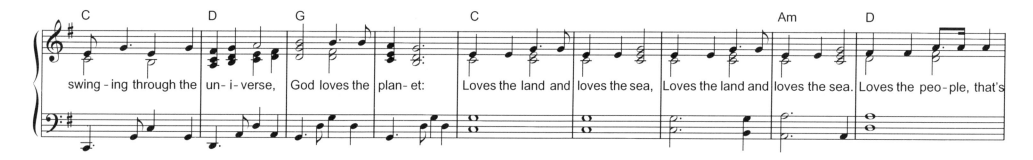

swing-ing through the un-i-verse, God loves the plan-et: Loves the land and loves the sea, Loves the land and loves the sea. Loves the peo-ple, that's

Words and Music © 1995 Stainer & Bell Ltd and The Trustees for Methodist Church Purposes

1 Big blue planet, swinging through the universe,
Big blue planet; what can it be? what can it be?
It's the planet earth, it's the planet earth.
It's the planet earth, it's the planet earth.

2 Big blue planet, swinging through the universe,
Big blue planet; what can we see? what can we see?
The great blue waters and the great green land.
The great blue waters and the great green land.

3 God's blue planet, swinging through the universe,
God's blue planet, what does God see? what does God see?
All the people of the world, all the people of the world,
All the people of the world, all the people of the world.

4 Poor blue planet, swinging through the universe,
Poor blue planet:
Water all soiled, land all spoiled,
Water all soiled, land all spoiled.
And the people are sad, and the people are sad,
And the people are sad, and the people are sad.

5 Big blue planet, swinging through the universe,
God loves the planet:
Loves the land and loves the sea,
Loves the land and loves the sea.
Loves the people, that's you and me,
Loves the people, that's you and me.
We'll love it too, it's our planet EARTH,
We'll love it too, it's our planet EARTH.

June Baker (1936–)

This, the title song of the book, was inspired by pictures of the earth taken from space. If possible, have one of these available as you sing. Sing the first line and the beginning of the second line of each verse together. Divide into two groups for the rest of the song, or ask the children to echo the leader or an older child. Introduce the song to people of all ages.

63 GOD MADE THE HEAVENS AND EARTH

Jo Doré (1949–)
arranged June Baker (1936–)

With swing, Latin American style

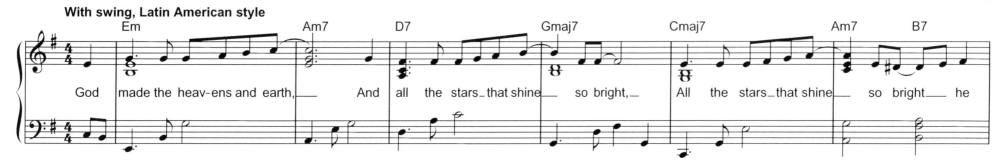

God made the heav-ens and earth,__ And all the stars_that shine__ so bright,__ All the stars_that shine__ so bright__ he

made. God made the day and the night,__ And all the min-utes that tick__ a - way,__

All the min-utes that tick__ a - way__ he made. *And I thank you__ Lord__ for your cre -*

Words and Music © 1995 Stainer & Bell Ltd and The Trustees for Methodist Church Purposes

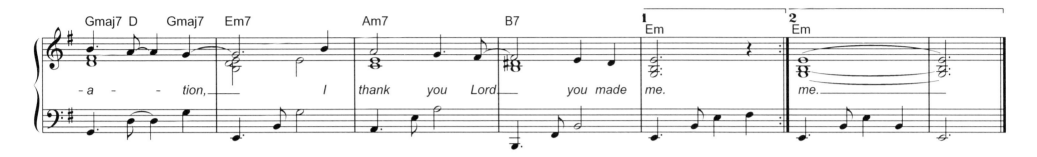

1   God made the heavens and earth,
     And all the stars that shine so bright,
     All the stars that shine so bright he made.
     God made the day and the night,
     And all the minutes that tick away,
     All the minutes that tick away he made.
     And I thank you Lord for your creation,
     I thank you Lord you made me.

2   God made the clear bright sky,
     And all the birds that fly about,
     All the birds that fly about he made.
     God made the deep blue sea,
     And all the fish that swim around.
     All the fish that swim around he made.
     Chorus

3   God made the rich red earth,
     And all the trees and flowers that grow,
     All the trees and flowers that grow he made.
     God made the family of man,
     And all the animals in this world,
     All the animals in this world he made.
     Chorus

Jo Doré (1949–)

Make the most of this lively rhythm and ask a good bongo player to join in where possible. Sing the verses as solos, or with a small choir, asking everyone to sing the chorus.

64 PWY RODDODD LIWIAU TLWS I'R WAWR?
WHO PUT THE WHITE IN THE CLOUDS?

Elwyn Jones (1928–)

1 Pwy roddodd liwiau tlws i'r wawr?
   Pwy roddodd las i'r moroedd mawr?
   Pwy roddodd wyn i'r eira ar lawr?
   Duw, rhoddwn gân o fawl i Ti.

2 Pwy roddodd heulwen yn y nen?
   Pwy roddodd wenyn uwch ein pen?
   Pwy roddodd afal ar y pren?
   Duw, rhoddwn gân o fawl i Ti.

3 Pwy yrrodd law i ddyfrhau y tir?
   Pwy yrrodd haul i wenu'n glir?
   Pwy wnaeth i'r ŷd aeddfedu cyn hir,
   Duw, rhoddwn gân o fawl i Ti.

Elwyn Jones (1928–)

1 Who put the white in the clouds so free?
   Who put the blue in the waves of the sea?
   Who put the green in the leaves of the tree?
   Lord, for these gifts we sing your praise.

2 Who made the sunshine and the breeze?
   Who made the busy, buzzing bees?
   Who made the apples on the trees?
   Lord, for these gifts we sing your praise.

3 Who sent the rain down from the sky?
   Who sent the sunshine by and by?
   Who made the corn to grow so high?
   Lord, for these gifts we sing your praise.

English Translation Elwyn Jones (1928–)

Words and Music © 1995 Stainer & Bell Ltd and The Trustees for Methodist Church Purposes

Encourage the children to paint large pictures of all the aspects of creation mentioned in the song and to hold them up as they sing.

65 GOD MADE FURRY THINGS

Penny Bury (1942–)
arranged June Baker (1936–)

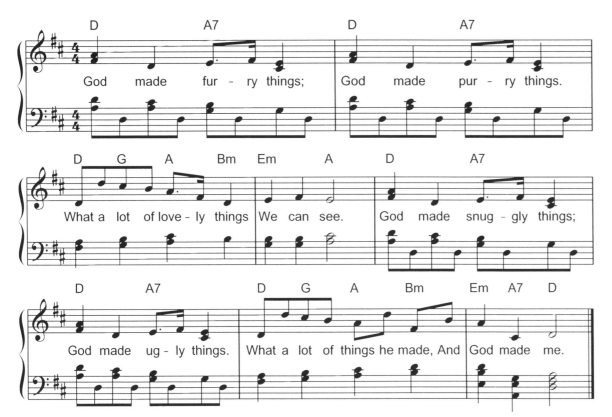

1   God made furry things;
    God made purry things.
    What a lot of lovely things
    We can see.
    God made snuggly things;
    God made ugly things.
    What a lot of things he made,
    And God made me.

2   God made sleepy things;
    God made creepy things.
    What a lot of lovely things
    He made too.
    God made gooey things;
    God made chewy things.
    What a lot of things he made,
    And God made you!

Penny Bury (1942–)

Words and Music © 1995 Stainer & Bell Ltd and The Trustees for Methodist Church Purposes

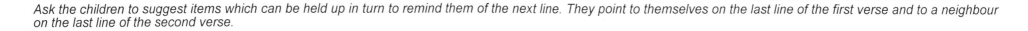

Ask the children to suggest items which can be held up in turn to remind them of the next line. They point to themselves on the last line of the first verse and to a neighbour on the last line of the second verse.

66 HERE COME THE FROGS

Peter Churchill (1963–)

1 Here come the frogs, hopping on the pond,
   (three times)
   Hop! Hop! Hop! Hop! Hop! *(jump or hop)*

2 Here come the waves, crashing on the beach,
   (three times)
   Crash! Crash! Crash! Crash! Crash! *(clap hands)*

3 Here come the birds pecking on the ground,
   (three times)
   Peck! Peck! Peck! Peck! Peck! *(one hand
   pecks on the other palm)*

4 Here comes the worm squirming in the soil,
   (three times)
   Squirm! Squirm! Squirm! Squirm! Squirm!
   (squirming hand movement)

5 Here come the children, shouting in the park,
   (three times)
   Shout! Shout! Shout! Shout! Shout!
   (cup hands round mouth)

6 Here comes Jesus, living in our hearts,
   (three times)
   Dance! Dance! Dance! Dance! Dance! *(dance)*

Peter Churchill (1963–) and Sophie Churchill (1963–)

Words and Music © Red Lentil Music from *Feeling Good!* published by The National Society. Used by permission.

This song reinforces the idea that God comes to us through our experience of the created world.

67   JUST A TINY SEED

Tracey Atkins (1965–)

1   Just a tiny seed,
    In the earth it goes,
    Just a little rain.
    It begins to grow.

2   From that tiny seed
    Grows a mighty tree,
    Branches spread out wide
    Shelter you and me.

3   In that mighty tree
    Birds will perch and sing.
    Like the tree, God's love
    From small seeds can spring.

Richard Atkins (1953–) and Andrew E Pratt (1948–)

Words and Music © 1995 Stainer & Bell Ltd and The Trustees for Methodist Church Purposes

Sing this song antiphonally — out-of-doors and under a large tree. Give each child a seed to hold and to take home. Alternatively, make together a large picture of a tree, as tall as possible. The children can pretend to be trees growing as they sing.

68 'CHEEP!' SAID THE SPARROW

Estelle White (1925–)

1 'Cheep!' said the sparrow on the chimney top,
  'All my feathers are known to God.'
  'Caw!' said the rook in a tree so tall,
  'I know that God gladly made us all.'

2 'Coo!' said the gentle one, the grey-blue dove,
  'I can tell you that God is love.'
  High up above sang the lark in flight,
  'I know the Lord is my heart's delight.'

3 'Chirp!' said the robin with his breast so red,
  'I don't work at all, yet I'm fed.'
  'Whoo!' called the owl in a leafy wood,
  'Our God is wonderful, wise and good.'

Estelle White (1925–)

Words and Music © 1977 Kevin Mayhew Ltd. Used by permission from *Many Ways to Praise*, Licence No. 498051.

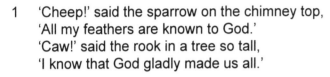

For a special occasion suggest the children make masks to wear, taking the parts of different birds.

WEATHER DAYS

69 MORNING, EVENING, FROST AND DEW

Doreen Newport (1927–)

1 Morning, evening, frost and dew,
Calm and storm and skies so blue,
Lord Jesus, these tell us
You keep making all things new.

2 Red sun shining down on me,
Warm and wonderful and free,
Lord Jesus, please fill us
With your light and energy.

3 Wild wind blowing fresh and strong,
Whipping all the leaves along,
Lord Jesus, please help us
Hear your power in its song.

4 Creamy clouds go sailing by,
Making mountains in the sky,
Lord Jesus, please keep us
Gentle like the clouds on high.

5 Lightning, thunder, whizz-bang-crash,
Raindrops, hailstones, splish-splosh-splash.
Lord Jesus, please quieten us
So we're never loud or brash.

6 Snowflakes falling on the ground,
Drifting down without a sound.
Lord Jesus, please come to us
Help us spread your peace around.

7 Wind and rain and hot sun's rays,
Silver nights and golden days,
Lord Jesus, please give us
Hearts and lives to sing your praise.

Doreen Newport (1927–)

Words and Music © 1995 Stainer & Bell Ltd and The Trustees for Methodist Church Purposes

The weather, famously unpredictable, makes this song an ideal introduction to the variety of God's created world. Sing it all the way through, or select verses to suit a particular day or theme.

70 I LIKE THE SUNSHINE

Traditional arranged Bruce Tulloch (1944–)

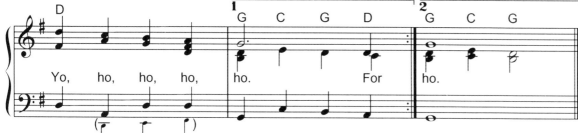

1   I like the sunshine,
    I like the rain,
    I like the wind and snow.
    Any kind of weather,
    It's all right by me,
    Yo, ho, ho, ho, ho.

2   For God made the sunshine,
    God made the rain,
    God made the wind and snow.
    Any kind of weather,
    It's all right by me,
    Yo, ho, ho, ho, ho.

Traditional

Arrangement © 1995 Stainer & Bell Ltd and The Trustees for Methodist Church Purposes

Children of all ages, including the very young, enjoy this song, especially the slide on 'sn-ow', which they can exaggerate as much as they like. For a particular occasion suggest that they bring sun hats, rain hats and scarves and take them on and off at the appropriate times in the song.

71 HOW BEAUTIFUL

Peter Churchill (1963–)

How beautiful, how beautiful,
How beautiful our world. *(twice)*

It's (springtime) now, it's (springtime) now,
So thank you for our world. *(twice)*

Leader For the lambs and fluffy ducklings
Children Thank you for our world.
Leader For the buds that open wide
Children Thank you for our world.

How beautiful, how beautiful,
How beautiful our world. *(twice)*

Suggested verses for other seasons:

Leader For the sea and sandy beaches
Children Thank you for our world.
Leader For the blue sky and the sunshine
Children Thank you for our world.

Leader For the falling of the leaves
Children Thank you for our world.
Leader For brown and shiny conkers
Children Thank you for our world.

Leader For the frosty grass in the morning
Children Thank you for our world.
Leader For the slippery frozen puddles
Children Thank you for your world.

Peter Churchill (1963–) and Sophie Churchill (1963–)

Words and Music © Red Lentil Music from *Feeling Good!* published by the National Society. Used by permission.

Each season is represented by a different version of this song. Encourage everyone to choose the things for which they wish to say thank you — the suggestions are just a starting point. The result is a prayer in which all can share.

SAD DAYS

72 DOMINE DEUS

Sylvia Crowther (1946–)

Domine Deus, *(raise one hand to waist level)*
Domine Deus, *(raise the other hand)*
Domine Deus, *(raise both hands further)*
Grant us peace. *(hands gently together)*

Words: Albert Jewell (1936–)
Actions: Sylvia Crowther (1946–)

Words and Music © 1995 Stainer & Bell Ltd and The Trustees for Methodist Church Purposes

Young children will love to get their mouths round the Latin words, which mean 'O Lord God'. Use this song after prayers of confession or prayers for others, or linked to the sharing of the Peace.

73   *I'M SITTING BY MYSELF*

June Baker (1936–)

1   I'm sitting by myself and I'm feeling very sad,
    Oh dear, oh dear;
    I'm sitting by myself and I'm feeling very sad,
    What shall I do?

2   I'm looking for a friend, and I'm feeling very shy,
    Oh dear, oh dear;
    I'm looking for a friend, and I'm feeling very shy,
    What shall I do?

3   I'll go and find a friend, 'stead of sitting by myself,
    Here I come, here I come;
    I'll go and find a friend who is sitting by him/herself,
    Here I come!

June Baker (1936–)

Words and Music © 1995 Stainer & Bell Ltd and The Trustees for Methodist Church Purposes

This song tries to help children who feel lonely and rejected to face some of their fears and to do something about them. At the end of the song all the children can go and sit by somebody else. Take special care that no children are left on their own.

74 WHEN I'M FEELING DOWN AND SAD

Joy Webb (1932–)

Gently, but not too slowly

When I'm feel-ing down and sad,

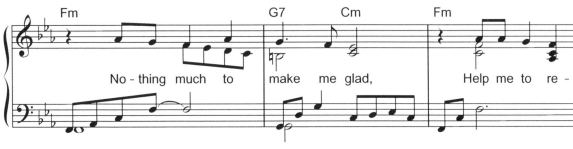

No-thing much to make me glad, Help me to re-

-mem-ber, you are There for me.

1 When I'm feeling down and sad,
Nothing much to make me glad,
Help me to remember, you are
There for me.

2 When things seem so diff'rent, and
Very hard to understand
Help me to remember, you are
Close to me.

3 When no-one has time for me,
Nothing's like it used to be,
Help me to remember, you are
Still with me.

4 When I'm crying, deep inside,
Harder than I've ever cried
Help me to remember, you are
Loving me.

Joy Webb (1932–)

Words and Music © 1995 Stainer & Bell Ltd and The Trustees for Methodist Church Purposes

Sadness is felt by everybody at some time, which makes this song suitable for both adults and children. It can be sung as a solo, then repeated by the group.

75 IT'S HARD TO SAY 'I'M SORRY'

Joy Webb (1932–)

1 It's hard to say 'I'm sorry', 'I'm sorry',
   When I've been in the wrong;
   But Jesus will be with me, be with me,
   And help me to be strong,
   I'll say 'I'm sorry', 'I'm sorry',
   'I'm sorry, yes I am'.

2 It's good to mean 'I'm sorry', 'I'm sorry',
   A grown up thing to do,
   And Jesus will be with me, be with me,
   To help his child right through,
   I'll say 'I'm sorry', 'I'm sorry',
   'I'm sorry, yes I am'.

3 If I can say 'I'm sorry', 'I'm sorry',
   And be forgiving too,
   Then Jesus will be happy, be happy,
   His child is being true,
   I'll say 'I'm sorry', 'I'm sorry',
   'I'm sorry, yes I am'.

Joy Webb (1932–)

Words and Music © 1995 Stainer & Bell Ltd and The Trustees for Methodist Church Purposes

An individual plea for forgiveness can also be the focus for a request by the whole group — as in this song.

HAPPY DAYS

76   WE ALL MARCH TO THE BEATING DRUM

Doreen Cocks (1926–)

1   We all march to the beating drum,
     March, march, march to the beating drum.
     Marching, marching, march, do not run,
     Marching with Jesus, having fun!
     We are marching and playing in your band,
     March with Jesus over all the land.
     Marching, marching, march, do not run,
     Marching with Jesus, having fun!

2   We all play on the ringing bells,
     March, march, march to the ringing bells.
     Marching, marching, march, do not run,
     Marching with Jesus, having fun!
     Chorus

3   We all ting on the triangle,
     March, march, march to the triangle.
     Marching, marching, march, do not run,
     Marching with Jesus, having fun!
     Chorus

4   We all tap on the tambourine,
     March, march, march to the tambourine.
     Marching, marching, march, do not run,
     Marching with Jesus, having fun!
     Chorus

5   We all play on the wooden sticks,
     March, march, march to the wooden sticks.
     Marching, marching, march, do not run,
     Marching with Jesus, having fun!
     Chorus

Elsie Grounds (1935–)

Words and Music © 1995 Stainer & Bell Ltd and The Trustees for Methodist Church Purposes

This piece needs a strong marching rhythm, which can be emphasised by using the appropriate percussion instruments for each verse.

77 I JUMP FOR JOY

Marjorie Waine (1916–)

1   I jump for joy as each new day dawns,
     I jump, jump, jump for joy.
     I jump for joy as each new day dawns,
     I jump, jump, jump for joy.
     Jump for joy, jump, jump, jump,
     I jump, jump, jump for joy.
     I jump for joy as each new day dawns,
     I jump, jump, jump for joy.

2   When I see a rainbow in the sky,
     I jump, jump, jump for joy.
     When I see a rainbow in the sky,
     I jump, jump, jump for joy.
     Jump for joy, jump, jump, jump,
     I jump, jump, jump for joy.
     When I see a rainbow in the sky,
     I jump, jump, jump for joy.

3   When I see the snowflakes falling down,
     I jump, jump, jump for joy.
     When I see the snowflakes falling down,
     I jump, jump, jump for joy.
     Jump for joy, jump, jump, jump,
     I jump, jump, jump for joy.
     When I see the snowflakes falling down,
     I jump, jump, jump for joy.

Marjorie Waine (1916–)

Words and Music © 1995 Stainer & Bell Ltd and The Trustees for Methodist Church Purposes

With very young children try using only the verses, and substitute different actions such as hopping or leaping.

78 JESUS IS MY FRIEND

Jo Doré (1949–)

Words and Music © 1995 Stainer & Bell Ltd and The Trustees for Methodist Church Purposes

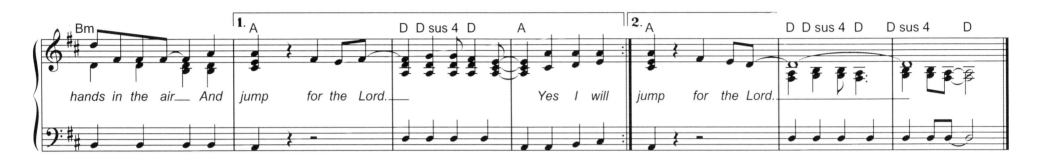

Jesus is my friend,
He walks with me wherever I go,
Jesus is my friend,
He talks with me and he lets me know
That he loves me,
Yes he loves me,
I'm happy, so I'll sing—

I will sing for the Lord,
Dance for the Lord,
Throw my hands in the air
And jump for the Lord.
Yes I will sing for the Lord,
Dance for the Lord,
Throw my hands in the air
And jump for the Lord.

Jo Doré (1949–)

This rock-style song should be performed with a strong beat and with a fairly free interpretation of the music. The actions in the chorus add to the fun

79 I LOVE THE PIT, PIT, PATTER OF THE RAINDROPS

Traditional arranged Bruce Tulloch (1944–)

I love the pit, pit, patter of the raindrops,
I love the buzz, buzz, buzzing of the bees.
But the thing I like the best, the very, very best,
Is to know that God loves me.

Traditional

I love the pit, pit, pat-ter of the rain-drops, I love the buzz, buzz, buzz-ing of the bees. But the thing I like the best, the ve-ry, ve-ry best, Is to know that God loves me.

Arrangement © 1995 Stainer & Bell Ltd and The Trustees for Methodist Church Purposes

Sing this verse several times before making up some new verses together, concentrating on sounds heard in nature.

80 I LIKE EATING

Peter Churchill (1963–)

1   I like eating *(Leader, then Children)*
Sandwiches and cakes
Toast and marmite
Crisps and chocolate flakes
Chips and baked beans
Strawberry icecream
Thank you God for food.

2   I like playing
Banging on a drum
Stories with Daddy
Painting with my Mum
Watering flowers
Building towers
Thank you God for fun.

3   I like people
Children that I meet
Friends at playgroup
People in the street
Fathers and mothers
Sisters and brothers
Thank you God for love.

*Peter Churchill (1963–) and
Sophie Churchill (1963–)*

Words and Music © Red Lentil Music from *Feeling Good!* published by The National Society. Used by permission.

Even though there are many words in this song, it can be enjoyed by very young children on account of the echo. Use it for all kinds of circumstances, such as a grace before a meal or a party, or as a celebration for Mothering Sunday or Father's Day.

81 IF YOU'RE BLACK OR IF YOU'RE WHITE

Traditional arranged Bruce Tulloch (1944–)

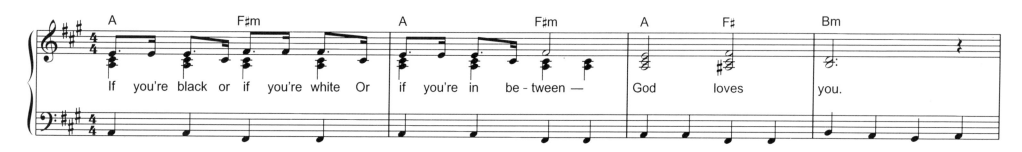

If you're black or if you're white Or if you're in be-tween — God loves you.

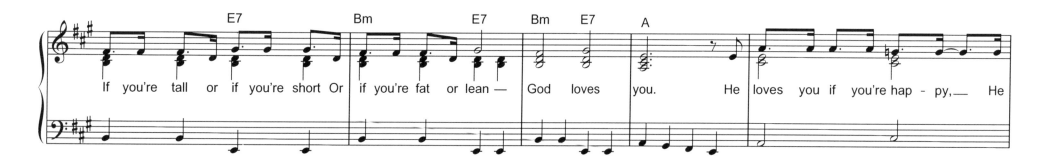

If you're tall or if you're short Or if you're fat or lean — God loves you. He loves you if you're hap-py,— He

loves you if you're sad, He loves you if you're feel-ing good, And ev-en if you're bad! No mat-ter what you look like,— No

Arrangement © 1995 Stainer & Bell Ltd and The Trustees for Methodist Church Purposes

mat - ter what you do — God loves you (you'd bet-ter be-lieve it!)__ God loves you.

If you're black or if you're white
Or if you're in between—
God loves you.
If you're tall or if you're short
Or if you're fat or lean—
God loves you.

He loves you if you're happy,
He loves you if you're sad,
He loves you if you're feeling good,
And even if you're bad!

No matter what you look like,
No matter what you do—
God loves you (you'd better believe it!) —
God loves you.

Traditional

A happy song in an attractive, popular style. The dotted rhythms should be made to swing lazily like jazz.

82 FOR MICRO CHIPS, FOR OVEN CHIPS

June Baker (1936–)

Words and Music © 1995 Stainer & Bell Ltd and The Trustees for Methodist Church Purposes

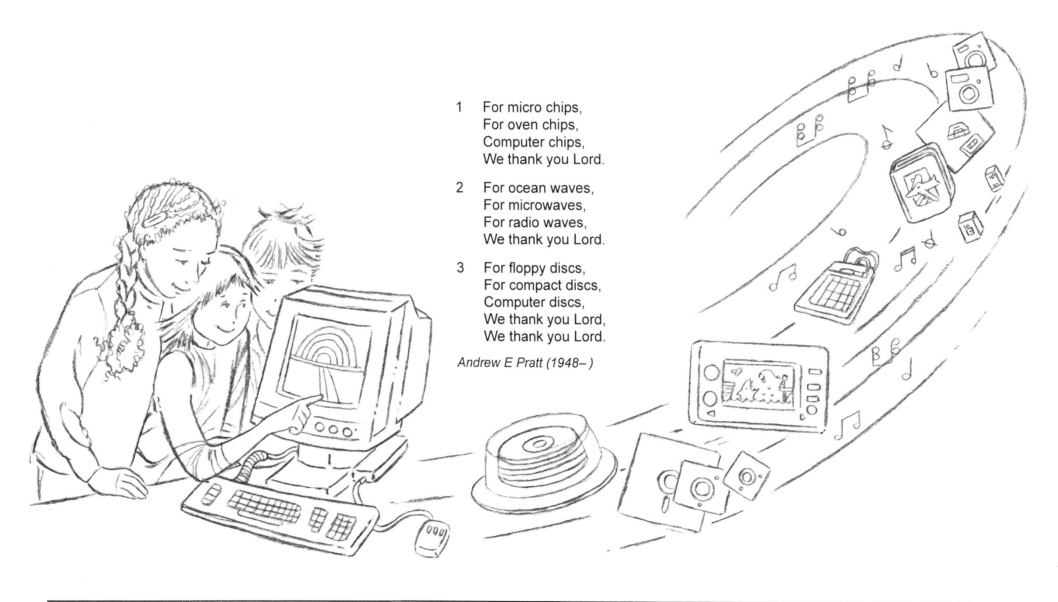

1   For micro chips,
    For oven chips,
    Computer chips,
    We thank you Lord.

2   For ocean waves,
    For microwaves,
    For radio waves,
    We thank you Lord.

3   For floppy discs,
    For compact discs,
    Computer discs,
    We thank you Lord,
    We thank you Lord.

Andrew E Pratt (1948–)

A song which will probably mean more to children than to adults! It needs to be sung at a good speed with a strongly repeated bass line to emphasise the blues-rock idiom. Unpitched percussion or clapping will help to emphasise each beat.

83 I SAW A DIPLODOCUS

June Baker (1936–)

Words and Music © 1995 Stainer & Bell Ltd and The Trustees for Methodist Church Purposes

I saw a diplodocus
Standing by a crocus;
It looked so big,
The crocus looked so small.
But the crocus, it was glowing,
I knew that it was growing,
Growing, growing, growing, growing, growing.
Diplodocus, it was heading for a fall.

Like stegosaurs and pterosaurs,
Triceratops, tyrannosaurs,
Diplodocus, all at once I saw was gone.
But, like the little crocus,
That no-one seems to notice,
God helps us grow as each year goes along.

Andrew E Pratt (1948–)

The fact that most six-year-olds can name more dinosaurs than a room full of adults was the starting point for this song. Children can paint pictures of many different dinosaurs and hold them up or point to them as they sing. This song is also fun to act out — growing like the crocus and heading for a fall like the diplodocus.

INDEX OF FIRST LINES
(CHORUSES IN ITALICS)

INDEX OF AUTHORS, TRANSLATORS AND SOURCES

INDEX OF COMPOSERS, ARRANGERS AND SOURCES OF TUNES

INDEX OF THEMES

BIBLICAL CHARACTERS

THE CHURCH'S YEAR

WORSHIP